Higher Scores on Math Standard[...]
Grade 5 Answer Sheet

M000249225

STUDENT'S NAME				
LAST		FIRST	MI	

SCHOOL

TEACHER:

FEMALE ○   MALE ○

BIRTH DATE

MONTH	DAY	YEAR
Jan ○	⓪ ⓪	⓪ ⓪
Feb ○	① ①	① ①
Mar ○	② ②	② ②
Apr ○	③ ③	③ ③
May ○	④	④ ④
Jun ○	⑤	⑤ ⑤
Jul ○	⑥	⑥ ⑥
Aug ○	⑦	⑦ ⑦
Sep ○	⑧	⑧ ⑧
Oct ○	⑨	⑨ ⑨
Nov ○		
Dec ○		

GRADE   ② ③ ④ ⑤ ⑥

Higher Scores on Math Standardized Tests, Grade 5

© Steck-Vaughn Company

Pretest, part 1

1. Ⓐ Ⓑ Ⓒ Ⓓ
2. Ⓐ Ⓑ Ⓒ Ⓓ
3. Ⓐ Ⓑ Ⓒ Ⓓ
4. Ⓐ Ⓑ Ⓒ Ⓓ
5. Ⓐ Ⓑ Ⓒ Ⓓ
6. Ⓐ Ⓑ Ⓒ Ⓓ
7. Ⓐ Ⓑ Ⓒ Ⓓ
8. Ⓐ Ⓑ Ⓒ Ⓓ
9. Ⓐ Ⓑ Ⓒ Ⓓ
10. Ⓐ Ⓑ Ⓒ Ⓓ
11. Ⓐ Ⓑ Ⓒ Ⓓ
12. Ⓐ Ⓑ Ⓒ Ⓓ
13. Ⓐ Ⓑ Ⓒ Ⓓ
14. Ⓐ Ⓑ Ⓒ Ⓓ
15. Ⓐ Ⓑ Ⓒ Ⓓ
16. Ⓐ Ⓑ Ⓒ Ⓓ
17. Ⓐ Ⓑ Ⓒ Ⓓ
18. Ⓐ Ⓑ Ⓒ Ⓓ
19. Ⓐ Ⓑ Ⓒ Ⓓ
20. Ⓐ Ⓑ Ⓒ Ⓓ
21. Ⓐ Ⓑ Ⓒ Ⓓ
22. Ⓐ Ⓑ Ⓒ Ⓓ
23. Ⓐ Ⓑ Ⓒ Ⓓ
24. Ⓐ Ⓑ Ⓒ Ⓓ
25. Ⓐ Ⓑ Ⓒ Ⓓ
26. Ⓐ Ⓑ Ⓒ Ⓓ
27. Ⓐ Ⓑ Ⓒ Ⓓ

Pretest, part 2

1. Ⓐ Ⓑ Ⓒ Ⓓ
2. Ⓐ Ⓑ Ⓒ Ⓓ
3. Ⓐ Ⓑ Ⓒ Ⓓ
4. Ⓐ Ⓑ Ⓒ Ⓓ
5. Ⓐ Ⓑ Ⓒ Ⓓ
6. Ⓐ Ⓑ Ⓒ Ⓓ
7. Ⓐ Ⓑ Ⓒ Ⓓ
8. Ⓐ Ⓑ Ⓒ Ⓓ
9. Ⓐ Ⓑ Ⓒ Ⓓ
10. Ⓐ Ⓑ Ⓒ Ⓓ
11. Ⓐ Ⓑ Ⓒ Ⓓ
12. Ⓐ Ⓑ Ⓒ Ⓓ
13. Ⓐ Ⓑ Ⓒ Ⓓ
14. Ⓐ Ⓑ Ⓒ Ⓓ
15. Ⓐ Ⓑ Ⓒ Ⓓ
16. Ⓐ Ⓑ Ⓒ Ⓓ
17. Ⓐ Ⓑ Ⓒ Ⓓ
18. Ⓐ Ⓑ Ⓒ Ⓓ
19. Ⓐ Ⓑ Ⓒ Ⓓ
20. Ⓐ Ⓑ Ⓒ Ⓓ

Posttest, part 1

1. Ⓐ Ⓑ Ⓒ Ⓓ
2. Ⓐ Ⓑ Ⓒ Ⓓ
3. Ⓐ Ⓑ Ⓒ Ⓓ
4. Ⓐ Ⓑ Ⓒ Ⓓ
5. Ⓐ Ⓑ Ⓒ Ⓓ
6. Ⓐ Ⓑ Ⓒ Ⓓ
7. Ⓐ Ⓑ Ⓒ Ⓓ
8. Ⓐ Ⓑ Ⓒ Ⓓ
9. Ⓐ Ⓑ Ⓒ Ⓓ
10. Ⓐ Ⓑ Ⓒ Ⓓ
11. Ⓐ Ⓑ Ⓒ Ⓓ
12. Ⓐ Ⓑ Ⓒ Ⓓ
13. Ⓐ Ⓑ Ⓒ Ⓓ
14. Ⓐ Ⓑ Ⓒ Ⓓ
15. Ⓐ Ⓑ Ⓒ Ⓓ
16. Ⓐ Ⓑ Ⓒ Ⓓ
17. Ⓐ Ⓑ Ⓒ Ⓓ
18. Ⓐ Ⓑ Ⓒ Ⓓ
19. Ⓐ Ⓑ Ⓒ Ⓓ
20. Ⓐ Ⓑ Ⓒ Ⓓ
21. Ⓐ Ⓑ Ⓒ Ⓓ
22. Ⓐ Ⓑ Ⓒ Ⓓ
23. Ⓐ Ⓑ Ⓒ Ⓓ
24. Ⓐ Ⓑ Ⓒ Ⓓ
25. Ⓐ Ⓑ Ⓒ Ⓓ
26. Ⓐ Ⓑ Ⓒ Ⓓ
27. Ⓐ Ⓑ Ⓒ Ⓓ

Posttest, part 2

1. Ⓐ Ⓑ Ⓒ Ⓓ
2. Ⓐ Ⓑ Ⓒ Ⓓ
3. Ⓐ Ⓑ Ⓒ Ⓓ
4. Ⓐ Ⓑ Ⓒ Ⓓ
5. Ⓐ Ⓑ Ⓒ Ⓓ
6. Ⓐ Ⓑ Ⓒ Ⓓ
7. Ⓐ Ⓑ Ⓒ Ⓓ
8. Ⓐ Ⓑ Ⓒ Ⓓ
9. Ⓐ Ⓑ Ⓒ Ⓓ
10. Ⓐ Ⓑ Ⓒ Ⓓ
11. Ⓐ Ⓑ Ⓒ Ⓓ
12. Ⓐ Ⓑ Ⓒ Ⓓ
13. Ⓐ Ⓑ Ⓒ Ⓓ
14. Ⓐ Ⓑ Ⓒ Ⓓ
15. Ⓐ Ⓑ Ⓒ Ⓓ
16. Ⓐ Ⓑ Ⓒ Ⓓ
17. Ⓐ Ⓑ Ⓒ Ⓓ
18. Ⓐ Ⓑ Ⓒ Ⓓ
19. Ⓐ Ⓑ Ⓒ Ⓓ
20. Ⓐ Ⓑ Ⓒ Ⓓ

Lesson 1: Number Concepts

1. Ⓐ Ⓑ Ⓒ Ⓓ
2. Ⓐ Ⓑ Ⓒ Ⓓ
3. Ⓐ Ⓑ Ⓒ Ⓓ
4. Ⓐ Ⓑ Ⓒ Ⓓ
5. Ⓐ Ⓑ Ⓒ Ⓓ
6. Ⓐ Ⓑ Ⓒ Ⓓ
7. Ⓐ Ⓑ Ⓒ Ⓓ
8. Ⓐ Ⓑ Ⓒ Ⓓ
9. Ⓐ Ⓑ Ⓒ Ⓓ
10. Ⓐ Ⓑ Ⓒ Ⓓ
11. Ⓐ Ⓑ Ⓒ Ⓓ
12. Ⓐ Ⓑ Ⓒ Ⓓ
13. Ⓐ Ⓑ Ⓒ Ⓓ
14. Ⓐ Ⓑ Ⓒ Ⓓ
15. Ⓐ Ⓑ Ⓒ Ⓓ
16. Ⓐ Ⓑ Ⓒ Ⓓ
17. Ⓐ Ⓑ Ⓒ Ⓓ
18. Ⓐ Ⓑ Ⓒ Ⓓ
19. Ⓐ Ⓑ Ⓒ Ⓓ
20. Ⓐ Ⓑ Ⓒ Ⓓ

Lesson 1: Number Concepts (cont.)

21. Ⓐ Ⓑ Ⓒ Ⓓ 　 23. Ⓐ Ⓑ Ⓒ Ⓓ 　 25. Ⓐ Ⓑ Ⓒ Ⓓ 　 27. Ⓐ Ⓑ Ⓒ Ⓓ 　 29. Ⓐ Ⓑ Ⓒ Ⓓ
22. Ⓐ Ⓑ Ⓒ Ⓓ 　 24. Ⓐ Ⓑ Ⓒ Ⓓ 　 26. Ⓐ Ⓑ Ⓒ Ⓓ 　 28. Ⓐ Ⓑ Ⓒ Ⓓ 　 30. Ⓐ Ⓑ Ⓒ Ⓓ

Lesson 2: Whole Number Computation

1. Ⓐ Ⓑ Ⓒ Ⓓ 　 4. Ⓐ Ⓑ Ⓒ Ⓓ 　 7. Ⓐ Ⓑ Ⓒ Ⓓ 　 10. Ⓐ Ⓑ Ⓒ Ⓓ 　 13. Ⓐ Ⓑ Ⓒ Ⓓ
2. Ⓐ Ⓑ Ⓒ Ⓓ 　 5. Ⓐ Ⓑ Ⓒ Ⓓ 　 8. Ⓐ Ⓑ Ⓒ Ⓓ 　 11. Ⓐ Ⓑ Ⓒ Ⓓ 　 14. Ⓐ Ⓑ Ⓒ Ⓓ
3. Ⓐ Ⓑ Ⓒ Ⓓ 　 6. Ⓐ Ⓑ Ⓒ Ⓓ 　 9. Ⓐ Ⓑ Ⓒ Ⓓ 　 12. Ⓐ Ⓑ Ⓒ Ⓓ

Lesson 3: Estimation

1. Ⓐ Ⓑ Ⓒ Ⓓ 　 4. Ⓐ Ⓑ Ⓒ Ⓓ 　 7. Ⓐ Ⓑ Ⓒ Ⓓ 　 10. Ⓐ Ⓑ Ⓒ Ⓓ 　 13. Ⓐ Ⓑ Ⓒ Ⓓ
2. Ⓐ Ⓑ Ⓒ Ⓓ 　 5. Ⓐ Ⓑ Ⓒ Ⓓ 　 8. Ⓐ Ⓑ Ⓒ Ⓓ 　 11. Ⓐ Ⓑ Ⓒ Ⓓ 　 14. Ⓐ Ⓑ Ⓒ Ⓓ
3. Ⓐ Ⓑ Ⓒ Ⓓ 　 6. Ⓐ Ⓑ Ⓒ Ⓓ 　 9. Ⓐ Ⓑ Ⓒ Ⓓ 　 12. Ⓐ Ⓑ Ⓒ Ⓓ

Lesson 4: Fractions and Decimals

1. Ⓐ Ⓑ Ⓒ Ⓓ 　 7. Ⓐ Ⓑ Ⓒ Ⓓ 　 13. Ⓐ Ⓑ Ⓒ Ⓓ 　 19. Ⓐ Ⓑ Ⓒ Ⓓ 　 25. Ⓐ Ⓑ Ⓒ Ⓓ
2. Ⓐ Ⓑ Ⓒ Ⓓ 　 8. Ⓐ Ⓑ Ⓒ Ⓓ 　 14. Ⓐ Ⓑ Ⓒ Ⓓ 　 20. Ⓐ Ⓑ Ⓒ Ⓓ 　 26. Ⓐ Ⓑ Ⓒ Ⓓ
3. Ⓐ Ⓑ Ⓒ Ⓓ 　 9. Ⓐ Ⓑ Ⓒ Ⓓ 　 15. Ⓐ Ⓑ Ⓒ Ⓓ 　 21. Ⓐ Ⓑ Ⓒ Ⓓ 　 27. Ⓐ Ⓑ Ⓒ Ⓓ
4. Ⓐ Ⓑ Ⓒ Ⓓ 　 10. Ⓐ Ⓑ Ⓒ Ⓓ 　 16. Ⓐ Ⓑ Ⓒ Ⓓ 　 22. Ⓐ Ⓑ Ⓒ Ⓓ 　 28. Ⓐ Ⓑ Ⓒ Ⓓ
5. Ⓐ Ⓑ Ⓒ Ⓓ 　 11. Ⓐ Ⓑ Ⓒ Ⓓ 　 17. Ⓐ Ⓑ Ⓒ Ⓓ 　 23. Ⓐ Ⓑ Ⓒ Ⓓ 　 29. Ⓐ Ⓑ Ⓒ Ⓓ
6. Ⓐ Ⓑ Ⓒ Ⓓ 　 12. Ⓐ Ⓑ Ⓒ Ⓓ 　 18. Ⓐ Ⓑ Ⓒ Ⓓ 　 24. Ⓐ Ⓑ Ⓒ Ⓓ

Lesson 5: Ratios and Percents

1. Ⓐ Ⓑ Ⓒ Ⓓ 　 4. Ⓐ Ⓑ Ⓒ Ⓓ 　 7. Ⓐ Ⓑ Ⓒ Ⓓ 　 10. Ⓐ Ⓑ Ⓒ Ⓓ 　 13. Ⓐ Ⓑ Ⓒ Ⓓ
2. Ⓐ Ⓑ Ⓒ Ⓓ 　 5. Ⓐ Ⓑ Ⓒ Ⓓ 　 8. Ⓐ Ⓑ Ⓒ Ⓓ 　 11. Ⓐ Ⓑ Ⓒ Ⓓ 　 14. Ⓐ Ⓑ Ⓒ Ⓓ
3. Ⓐ Ⓑ Ⓒ Ⓓ 　 6. Ⓐ Ⓑ Ⓒ Ⓓ 　 9. Ⓐ Ⓑ Ⓒ Ⓓ 　 12. Ⓐ Ⓑ Ⓒ Ⓓ

Lesson 6: Measurement and Geometry

1. Ⓐ Ⓑ Ⓒ Ⓓ 　 7. Ⓐ Ⓑ Ⓒ Ⓓ 　 13. Ⓐ Ⓑ Ⓒ Ⓓ 　 19. Ⓐ Ⓑ Ⓒ Ⓓ 　 25. Ⓐ Ⓑ Ⓒ Ⓓ
2. Ⓐ Ⓑ Ⓒ Ⓓ 　 8. Ⓐ Ⓑ Ⓒ Ⓓ 　 14. Ⓐ Ⓑ Ⓒ Ⓓ 　 20. Ⓐ Ⓑ Ⓒ Ⓓ 　 26. Ⓐ Ⓑ Ⓒ Ⓓ
3. Ⓐ Ⓑ Ⓒ Ⓓ 　 9. Ⓐ Ⓑ Ⓒ Ⓓ 　 15. Ⓐ Ⓑ Ⓒ Ⓓ 　 21. Ⓐ Ⓑ Ⓒ Ⓓ 　 27. Ⓐ Ⓑ Ⓒ Ⓓ
4. Ⓐ Ⓑ Ⓒ Ⓓ 　 10. Ⓐ Ⓑ Ⓒ Ⓓ 　 16. Ⓐ Ⓑ Ⓒ Ⓓ 　 22. Ⓐ Ⓑ Ⓒ Ⓓ 　 28. Ⓐ Ⓑ Ⓒ Ⓓ
5. Ⓐ Ⓑ Ⓒ Ⓓ 　 11. Ⓐ Ⓑ Ⓒ Ⓓ 　 17. Ⓐ Ⓑ Ⓒ Ⓓ 　 23. Ⓐ Ⓑ Ⓒ Ⓓ 　 29. Ⓐ Ⓑ Ⓒ Ⓓ
6. Ⓐ Ⓑ Ⓒ Ⓓ 　 12. Ⓐ Ⓑ Ⓒ Ⓓ 　 18. Ⓐ Ⓑ Ⓒ Ⓓ 　 24. Ⓐ Ⓑ Ⓒ Ⓓ

Lesson 7: Statistics and Probability

1. Ⓐ Ⓑ Ⓒ Ⓓ 　 6. Ⓐ Ⓑ Ⓒ Ⓓ 　 11. Ⓐ Ⓑ Ⓒ Ⓓ 　 16. Ⓐ Ⓑ Ⓒ Ⓓ 　 21. Ⓐ Ⓑ Ⓒ Ⓓ
2. Ⓐ Ⓑ Ⓒ Ⓓ 　 7. Ⓐ Ⓑ Ⓒ Ⓓ 　 12. Ⓐ Ⓑ Ⓒ Ⓓ 　 17. Ⓐ Ⓑ Ⓒ Ⓓ 　 22. Ⓐ Ⓑ Ⓒ Ⓓ
3. Ⓐ Ⓑ Ⓒ Ⓓ 　 8. Ⓐ Ⓑ Ⓒ Ⓓ 　 13. Ⓐ Ⓑ Ⓒ Ⓓ 　 18. Ⓐ Ⓑ Ⓒ Ⓓ 　 23. Ⓐ Ⓑ Ⓒ Ⓓ
4. Ⓐ Ⓑ Ⓒ Ⓓ 　 9. Ⓐ Ⓑ Ⓒ Ⓓ 　 14. Ⓐ Ⓑ Ⓒ Ⓓ 　 19. Ⓐ Ⓑ Ⓒ Ⓓ 　 24. Ⓐ Ⓑ Ⓒ Ⓓ
5. Ⓐ Ⓑ Ⓒ Ⓓ 　 10. Ⓐ Ⓑ Ⓒ Ⓓ 　 15. Ⓐ Ⓑ Ⓒ Ⓓ 　 20. Ⓐ Ⓑ Ⓒ Ⓓ

Lesson 8: Pre-Algebra

1. Ⓐ Ⓑ Ⓒ Ⓓ 　 4. Ⓐ Ⓑ Ⓒ Ⓓ 　 7. Ⓐ Ⓑ Ⓒ Ⓓ 　 10. Ⓐ Ⓑ Ⓒ Ⓓ 　 13. Ⓐ Ⓑ Ⓒ Ⓓ
2. Ⓐ Ⓑ Ⓒ Ⓓ 　 5. Ⓐ Ⓑ Ⓒ Ⓓ 　 8. Ⓐ Ⓑ Ⓒ Ⓓ 　 11. Ⓐ Ⓑ Ⓒ Ⓓ 　 14. Ⓐ Ⓑ Ⓒ Ⓓ
3. Ⓐ Ⓑ Ⓒ Ⓓ 　 6. Ⓐ Ⓑ Ⓒ Ⓓ 　 9. Ⓐ Ⓑ Ⓒ Ⓓ 　 12. Ⓐ Ⓑ Ⓒ Ⓓ

Lesson 9: Problem-Solving Strategies

1. Ⓐ Ⓑ Ⓒ Ⓓ 　 5. Ⓐ Ⓑ Ⓒ Ⓓ 　 9. Ⓐ Ⓑ Ⓒ Ⓓ 　 13. Ⓐ Ⓑ Ⓒ Ⓓ 　 17. Ⓐ Ⓑ Ⓒ Ⓓ
2. Ⓐ Ⓑ Ⓒ Ⓓ 　 6. Ⓐ Ⓑ Ⓒ Ⓓ 　 10. Ⓐ Ⓑ Ⓒ Ⓓ 　 14. Ⓐ Ⓑ Ⓒ Ⓓ 　 18. Ⓐ Ⓑ Ⓒ Ⓓ
3. Ⓐ Ⓑ Ⓒ Ⓓ 　 7. Ⓐ Ⓑ Ⓒ Ⓓ 　 11. Ⓐ Ⓑ Ⓒ Ⓓ 　 15. Ⓐ Ⓑ Ⓒ Ⓓ 　 19. Ⓐ Ⓑ Ⓒ Ⓓ
4. Ⓐ Ⓑ Ⓒ Ⓓ 　 8. Ⓐ Ⓑ Ⓒ Ⓓ 　 12. Ⓐ Ⓑ Ⓒ Ⓓ 　 16. Ⓐ Ⓑ Ⓒ Ⓓ 　 20. Ⓐ Ⓑ Ⓒ Ⓓ

Lesson 10: Problem Solving

1. Ⓐ Ⓑ Ⓒ Ⓔ 　 6. Ⓐ Ⓑ Ⓒ Ⓓ 　 11. Ⓐ Ⓑ Ⓒ Ⓓ 　 16. Ⓐ Ⓑ Ⓒ Ⓓ 　 21. Ⓐ Ⓑ Ⓒ Ⓓ
2. Ⓐ Ⓑ Ⓒ Ⓓ 　 7. Ⓐ Ⓑ Ⓒ Ⓓ 　 12. Ⓐ Ⓑ Ⓒ Ⓓ 　 17. Ⓐ Ⓑ Ⓒ Ⓓ 　 22. Ⓐ Ⓑ Ⓒ Ⓓ
3. Ⓐ Ⓑ Ⓒ Ⓓ 　 8. Ⓐ Ⓑ Ⓒ Ⓓ 　 13. Ⓐ Ⓑ Ⓒ Ⓓ 　 18. Ⓐ Ⓑ Ⓒ Ⓓ 　 23. Ⓐ Ⓑ Ⓒ Ⓓ
4. Ⓐ Ⓑ Ⓒ Ⓓ 　 9. Ⓐ Ⓑ Ⓒ Ⓓ 　 14. Ⓐ Ⓑ Ⓒ Ⓓ 　 19. Ⓐ Ⓑ Ⓒ Ⓓ 　 24. Ⓐ Ⓑ Ⓒ Ⓓ
5. Ⓐ Ⓑ Ⓒ Ⓓ 　 10. Ⓐ Ⓑ Ⓒ Ⓓ 　 15. Ⓐ Ⓑ Ⓒ Ⓓ 　 20. Ⓐ Ⓑ Ⓒ Ⓓ 　 25. Ⓐ Ⓑ Ⓒ Ⓓ

Name _____   Date _____

Pretest, part 1

Your score: _____

 You have 30 minutes to complete this test.

Lesson 1: Number Concepts

Directions Darken the circle by the correct answer to each problem.

1. What does the 8 in 418,702 mean?
- Ⓐ ten thousands
- Ⓑ hundreds
- Ⓒ thousands
- Ⓓ tens

2. Which number will correctly complete the following number sentence?

$(3 + 6) + 7 = \square + 7$
- Ⓐ 3
- Ⓑ 6
- Ⓒ 9
- Ⓓ 13

3. Which numbers complete the number pattern?

15, 16, 18, 21, ____, ____, 36
- Ⓐ 22, 25
- Ⓑ 23, 24
- Ⓒ 24, 27
- Ⓓ 25, 30

4. What is the missing shape in this pattern?

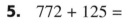
- Ⓐ circle
- Ⓑ square
- Ⓒ triangle
- Ⓓ star

Lesson 2: Whole Number Computation

Directions Darken the circle by the correct answer to each problem.

5. 772 + 125 =
- Ⓐ 997
- Ⓑ 897
- Ⓒ 887
- Ⓓ 647

6. 149 + 753 + 531 =
- Ⓐ 1,562
- Ⓑ 1,343
- Ⓒ 1,234
- Ⓓ 1,433

7. 318 – 66 =
- Ⓐ 252
- Ⓑ 352
- Ⓒ 242
- Ⓓ 384

8. 9,371 – 4,528 =
- Ⓐ 4,843
- Ⓑ 3,933
- Ⓒ 4,853
- Ⓓ 11,899

GO ON ⇨

Pretest, part 1, page 2

9. 49 × 38 =
Ⓐ 862
Ⓑ 1,962
Ⓒ 1,852
Ⓓ 1,862

10. 9 × 89 =
Ⓐ 901
Ⓑ 801
Ⓒ 723
Ⓓ 899 ·

11. 195 ÷ 3 =
Ⓐ 63
Ⓑ 85
Ⓒ 56
Ⓓ 65

12. 2,992 ÷ 8 =
Ⓐ 351
Ⓑ 374
Ⓒ 382
Ⓓ 329

Lesson 3: Estimation

Directions Darken the circle by the best estimate for each problem.

13. The closest estimate of 4,203 + 2,387 is between _____.
Ⓐ 4,500 and 5,800
Ⓑ 5,900 and 6,900
Ⓒ 7,000 and 7,500
Ⓓ 7,500 and 8,000

14. The closest estimate of 82 × 74 is _____.
Ⓐ 5,600
Ⓑ 6,200
Ⓒ 6,500
Ⓓ 7,000

15. The closest estimate of 7,189 ÷ 34 is between _____.
Ⓐ 20 and 30
Ⓑ 30 and 40
Ⓒ 100 and 150
Ⓓ 200 and 300

16. Tom and Nita drove an average of 210 kilometers a day on their 8-day vacation through Canada. Which is the best estimate of the total number of kilometers they drove on their trip?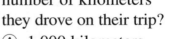
Ⓐ 1,000 kilometers
Ⓑ 1,600 kilometers
Ⓒ 2,000 kilometers
Ⓓ 2,500 kilometers

17. Students at Giddens Elementary School attend classes 175 days each year. So far this year, they have attended classes a total of 69 days. About how many days of school are left?
Ⓐ between 70 and 80 days
Ⓑ between 80 and 100 days
Ⓒ between 100 and 120 days
Ⓓ between 120 and 150 days

GO ON ⇨

Pretest, part 1, page 3

Lesson 4: Fractions and Decimals

Directions Darken the circle by the correct answer to each problem.

18.

$$\frac{4}{8}$$
$$-\frac{1}{8}$$

    Ⓐ $\frac{1}{8}$

    Ⓑ $\frac{3}{16}$

    Ⓒ $\frac{2}{8}$

    Ⓓ $\frac{3}{8}$

19.

$$\frac{1}{10}$$
$$+\frac{3}{5}$$

    Ⓐ $\frac{7}{10}$

    Ⓑ $\frac{6}{10}$

    Ⓒ $\frac{6}{20}$

    Ⓓ $\frac{8}{20}$

20. Reduce $\frac{5}{60}$ to its lowest term.

    Ⓐ $\frac{1}{15}$

    Ⓑ $\frac{5}{12}$

    Ⓒ $\frac{6}{15}$

    Ⓓ $\frac{1}{12}$

21. $19.07 + $67.92

    Ⓐ $96.88

    Ⓑ $96.99

    Ⓒ $100.09

    Ⓓ $86.99

22. $5.4 - 0.7$

    Ⓐ 6.1

    Ⓑ 4.7

    Ⓒ 5.3

    Ⓓ 5.7

23. 0.95×0.5

    Ⓐ 04.75

    Ⓑ 0.475

    Ⓒ 047.05

    Ⓓ 0.4705

Lesson 5: Ratios and Percents

Directions Darken the circle by the correct answer to each problem.

24. Which is the fraction for 20%?

    Ⓐ $\frac{3}{5}$

    Ⓑ $\frac{4}{5}$

    Ⓒ $\frac{1}{5}$

    Ⓓ $\frac{2}{5}$

25. A ratio is a way of _____ numbers.

    Ⓐ adding

    Ⓑ comparing

    Ⓒ dividing

    Ⓓ changing

26. Which is the decimal for 38%?

    Ⓐ 0.38

    Ⓑ 3.8

    Ⓒ 3.08

    Ⓓ 30.8

27. Which fraction shows a ratio of 25 to 1?

    Ⓐ $\frac{1}{25}$

    Ⓑ $1\frac{2}{5}$

    Ⓒ $\frac{25}{1}$

    Ⓓ $2\frac{5}{1}$

STOP

Name _____   Date _____

Pretest, part 2

Your score:_____

⏱ You have 30 minutes to complete this test.

Lesson 6: Measurement and Geometry

Directions Darken the circle by the correct answer to each question.

1. How many triangles are in this figure?

ⓐ 6
ⓑ 8
ⓒ 5
ⓓ 2

2. Which of these units are used to measure the length on a ruler?

ⓐ degrees
ⓑ kilograms
ⓒ centimeters
ⓓ liters

3. What is the perimeter of this figure?

ⓐ 36 inches
ⓑ 24 inches
ⓒ 18 inches
ⓓ 12 inches

h

← 6 in →

4. Which is the name for these lines?

ⓐ intersecting
ⓑ perpendicular
ⓒ parallel
ⓓ crooked

Lesson 7: Statistics and Probability

Directions Darken the circle by the correct answer to each question.

Use the graph to answer questions 5–6.

JUDY'S ALLOWANCE

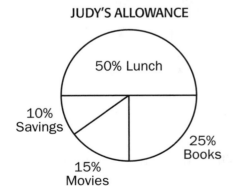

50% Lunch

10% Savings

15% Movies

25% Books

5. What percent of her allowance does Judy spend on books?

ⓐ 10%
ⓑ 25%
ⓒ 15%
ⓓ 35%

6. What percent of her allowance does Judy use for books, movies, and savings?

ⓐ 50%
ⓑ 10%
ⓒ 25%
ⓓ 15%

GO ON ⇨

Pretest, part 2, page 2

7. A bag contains 5 clear marbles and 10 colored marbles. What is the probability of reaching into the bag and pulling out a clear marble?

Ⓐ $\frac{10}{15}$

Ⓑ $\frac{7}{15}$

Ⓒ $\frac{5}{15}$

Ⓓ $\frac{3}{15}$

8. With his eyes closed, which card will Julio most likely pick?

Ⓐ A

Ⓑ B

Ⓒ C

Ⓓ D

Lesson 8: Pre-Algebra

Directions Darken the circle by the correct answer to each question.

9. If $x = 4$, then $x + 3 =$

Ⓐ 1 Ⓑ 7

Ⓒ 12 Ⓓ 43

10. If $130 + x = 420$, then $x =$

Ⓐ 550 Ⓑ 390

Ⓒ 290 Ⓓ 210

11. If $175 + x = 350$, then $x =$

Ⓐ 125 Ⓑ 150

Ⓒ 175 Ⓓ 525

12. If $y - 75 = 215$, then $y =$

Ⓐ 140 Ⓑ 270

Ⓒ 280 Ⓓ 290

Lesson 9: Problem-Solving Strategies

Directions Darken the circle by the best answer to each question.

13. A recipe calls for $2\frac{1}{4}$ cups of flour. The recipe makes 8 servings. How many cups of flour will be needed to make 24 servings?

What strategy should you use to solve this problem?

Ⓐ work backwards

Ⓑ use a multi-step plan

Ⓒ guess and check

Ⓓ make a pattern

14. Jessica's grandmother is 4 times older than Jessica. What else do you need to know to learn Jessica's age?

Ⓐ the age of Jessica's mother

Ⓑ the age of Jessica's grandmother

Ⓒ the age of Jessica's grandfather

Ⓓ whether Jessica is an only child

GO ON ⇨

Pretest, part 2, page 3

Lesson 10: Problem Solving

Directions Darken the circle by the correct answer to each problem.

15. One day last month the school cafeteria sold 178 ice-cream cones. The next day it sold 212 ice-cream cones. How many ice-cream cones were sold altogether?

Ⓐ 400
Ⓑ 390
Ⓒ 350
Ⓓ 420

16. Attendance at the championship soccer game was 3,458. This total included 100 complimentary tickets that were given away. How many people paid for their tickets?
Ⓐ 3,358
Ⓑ 3,458
Ⓒ 3,558
Ⓓ 13,458

17. Esther is filling 15 "loot bags" for her brother's birthday party. She will place 5 items inside each bag. How many items will she need to fill all the bags?
Ⓐ 25
Ⓑ 75
Ⓒ 20
Ⓓ 60

18. The Jolly Chefs Club planned to sell hamburgers at the craft fair. They bought 5,184 buns that came in boxes of 12 per box. How many boxes of buns did they have?
Ⓐ 432 boxes
Ⓑ 300 boxes
Ⓒ 520 boxes
Ⓓ 624 boxes

19. Admission to a theme park costs $24.50 per person. On Tuesdays the park has a special promotion that lets you buy a 5-pack of tickets for $98. How much money would a family of 5 save if they went to the park on Tuesday?
Ⓐ $24.50
Ⓑ $2.00
Ⓒ $4.50
Ⓓ $22.50

20. The Bonshaw River is about 180 kilometers long. French River is about 21 times as long. How long is French River?
Ⓐ 378 kilometers
Ⓑ 3,780 kilometers
Ⓒ 7,803 kilometers
Ⓓ 4,230 kilometers

STOP

Name _____ Date _____

Posttest, part 1

Your score:_____

⏱ **You have 30 minutes to complete this test.**

Lesson 1: Number Concepts

Directions Darken the circle by the correct answer to each problem.

1. In which number does the 3 stand for hundreds?
   Ⓐ 9,235
   Ⓑ 2,395
   Ⓒ 9,253
   Ⓓ 2,935

2. Which number would make the following number sentence correct?
   $(3 \times 4) + (6 \times 4) = \boxed{} \times 4$
   Ⓐ 3
   Ⓑ 6
   Ⓒ 9
   Ⓓ 18

3. Which numbers would be next in this pattern?
   4, 8, 16, _____, _____
   Ⓐ 32, 64
   Ⓑ 24, 32
   Ⓒ 20, 24
   Ⓓ 20, 28

4. Liz uses beads to make bracelets. She begins with 3 blue beads, then 6 brown beads, then 4 green beads, then 2 purple beads. If she repeats this pattern, what color will she use for the 24th bead?
   Ⓐ blue
   Ⓑ brown
   Ⓒ green
   Ⓓ purple

Lesson 2: Whole Number Computation

Directions Darken the circle by the correct answer to each problem.

5. 47 + 873 =
   Ⓐ 830
   Ⓑ 820
   Ⓒ 920
   Ⓓ 826

6. 4,075 + 279 + 3,457 =
   Ⓐ 7,801
   Ⓑ 7,811
   Ⓒ 7,001
   Ⓓ 897

7. 564 − 213 =
   Ⓐ 347
   Ⓑ 351
   Ⓒ 251
   Ⓓ 777

8. 680 − 213 =
   Ⓐ 3,677
   Ⓑ 367
   Ⓒ 467
   Ⓓ 893

GO ON ⇨

Posttest, part 1, page 2

9. $87 \times 47 =$
   Ⓐ 4,089   Ⓑ 4,890
   Ⓒ 5,089   Ⓓ 8,477

10. $237 \times 61 =$
   Ⓐ 1,659   Ⓑ 14,467
   Ⓒ 16,599   Ⓓ 14,457

11. $196 \div 5 =$
   Ⓐ 39 R1   Ⓑ 49
   Ⓒ 41 R1   Ⓓ 40

12. $48\overline{)1{,}594}$
   Ⓐ 33 R10   Ⓑ 34 R9
   Ⓒ 33 R8   Ⓓ 43

Lesson 3: Estimation

Directions Darken the circle by the best estimate for each problem.

13. The closest estimate of 525×67 is between _____.
   Ⓐ 34,000 and 36,000
   Ⓑ 25,000 and 28,000
   Ⓒ 22,000 and 24,000
   Ⓓ 20,000 and 22,000

14. The closest estimate of $3480 \div 68$ is _____.
   Ⓐ 30
   Ⓑ 40
   Ⓒ 50
   Ⓓ 60

15. The closest estimate of 345×43 is between _____.
   Ⓐ 17,000 and 18,000
   Ⓑ 14,000 and 15,000
   Ⓒ 10,000 and 11,000
   Ⓓ 5,000 and 6,000

16. Kim is the treasurer of the school drama club. She bought 14 theater tickets for the members of the drama club. Each ticket cost $15.75. What is the best estimate for the total cost of the tickets?
   Ⓐ $100
   Ⓑ $200
   Ⓒ $300
   Ⓓ $400

17. Vince buys a pack of baseball cards every week. He has over 620 cards. The cards are sold with 12 cards in each pack. About how many weeks has he been buying packs of cards?
   Ⓐ between 40 and 45
   Ⓑ between 50 and 60
   Ⓒ between 65 and 70
   Ⓓ between 70 and 80

GO ON ⇨

Posttest, part 1, page 3

Lesson 4: Fractions and Decimals

Directions Darken the circle by the correct answer to each problem.

18. $\frac{4}{9} \times 27 =$
- Ⓐ 108
- Ⓑ $4\frac{3}{9}$
- Ⓒ 12
- Ⓓ 3

19. $\frac{1}{3} \div \frac{3}{9} =$
- Ⓐ $\frac{5}{12}$
- Ⓑ $\frac{3}{4}$
- Ⓒ $\frac{9}{12}$
- Ⓓ 1

20. What is the lowest term for the answer to $\frac{13}{16} - \frac{5}{16}$?
- Ⓐ $\frac{8}{16}$
- Ⓑ $\frac{1}{2}$
- Ⓒ $\frac{3}{8}$
- Ⓓ $\frac{8}{12}$

21. $3.95 - 0.47$ ____.
- Ⓐ 2.48
- Ⓑ 3.58
- Ⓒ 3.48
- Ⓓ 3.42

22. Which number sentence is true?
- Ⓐ $0.52 < 0.39$
- Ⓑ $0.07 < 0.081$
- Ⓒ $0.539 < 0.099$
- Ⓓ $0.402 < 0.008$

23. $9\overline{)64.17}$
- Ⓐ 0.713
- Ⓑ 7.13
- Ⓒ 71.3
- Ⓓ 73.17

Lesson 5: Ratios and Percents

Directions Darken the circle by the correct answer to each problem.

24. Which pair of ratios is equal?
- Ⓐ $\frac{3}{1}$, $\frac{12}{4}$
- Ⓑ $\frac{3}{2}$, $\frac{6}{10}$
- Ⓒ $\frac{3}{2}$, $\frac{7}{4}$
- Ⓓ $\frac{9}{6}$, $\frac{12}{18}$

25. Which percent equals 17/100?
- Ⓐ 70%
- Ⓑ 17%
- Ⓒ 100%
- Ⓓ 71%

26. The gardener has finished mowing $\frac{1}{4}$ of the lawn. What percent of the lawn is finished?
- Ⓐ 25%
- Ⓑ 40%
- Ⓒ 75%
- Ⓓ 80%

27. Use 50% to estimate 53% of 244.
- Ⓐ 122
- Ⓑ 53
- Ⓒ 104
- Ⓓ 200

STOP

Name _____ Date _____

Posttest, part 2

Your score: _____

⏱ **You have 30 minutes to complete this test.**

Lesson 6: Measurement and Geometry

Directions Darken the circle by the correct answer to each problem.

1. What units are used to measure mass or weight on a scale?
   - Ⓐ meters
   - Ⓑ milliliters
   - Ⓒ grams
   - Ⓓ degrees

2. Bernard cut a rectangle that was 6 inches wide and 12 inches long into 2 squares. What was the perimeter of each of the squares?
   - Ⓐ 48 inches
   - Ⓑ 36 inches
   - Ⓒ 24 inches
   - Ⓓ 18 inches

3. What is the radius of the circle shown here?
   - Ⓐ 3 in.
   - Ⓑ 6 in.
   - Ⓒ 9 in.
   - Ⓓ 12 in.

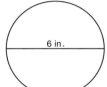
6 in.

4. Find the area of a rectangle that is 4 meters by 8 meters.
   - Ⓐ 12 m^2
   - Ⓑ 24 m^2
   - Ⓒ 36 m^2
   - Ⓓ 32 m^2

Lesson 7: Statistics and Probability

Directions Darken the circle by the correct answer to each question.

Use the graph to answer questions 5–6.

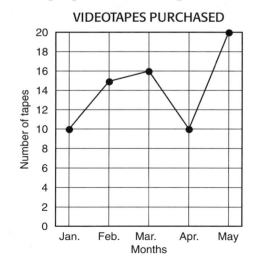

VIDEOTAPES PURCHASED

5. In what month did sales go down?
   - Ⓐ February
   - Ⓑ March
   - Ⓒ April
   - Ⓓ May

6. How many tapes were sold in February and March?
   - Ⓐ 16 tapes
   - Ⓑ 31 tapes
   - Ⓒ 15 tapes
   - Ⓓ 25 tapes

GO ON ⇨

Posttest, part 2, page 2

Answer question 7 using these cards.

7. What is the probability of choosing a card with the letter A?

Ⓐ $\frac{9}{10}$

Ⓑ $\frac{1}{5}$

Ⓒ $\frac{1}{10}$

Ⓓ $\frac{2}{5}$

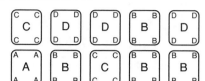

8. Kim's favorite word game uses the spinner shown here. What is the probability that the spinner will land on a vowel?

Ⓐ $\frac{2}{8}$

Ⓑ $\frac{3}{8}$

Ⓒ $\frac{4}{8}$

Ⓓ $\frac{5}{8}$

Lesson 8: Pre-Algebra

Directions Darken the circle by the best answer to each question.

9. If $125 + x = 650$, then x =

Ⓐ 755

Ⓑ 625

Ⓒ 525

Ⓓ 475

10. If $27 \div y = 3$, then y =

Ⓐ 6

Ⓑ 12

Ⓒ 9

Ⓓ 18

11. If $x \div 8 = 10$, then x =

Ⓐ 8

Ⓑ 16

Ⓒ 40

Ⓓ 80

12. If $x - 100 = 45$, then x =

Ⓐ 55

Ⓑ 145

Ⓒ 155

Ⓓ 255

Lesson 9: Problem-Solving Strategies

Directions Darken the circle by the best strategy to solve each problem.

13. Mrs. Gomez sells dictionaries. Yesterday she sold 11 books and earned $132. How much did each book cost?

Ⓐ find the pattern

Ⓑ make a list

Ⓒ make a table

Ⓓ choose an operation

14. Bus fare from Johnson City to Palmerville is $1.25. What do you need to know to find out if Vanessa and her friends can get from Johnson City to Palmerville with $10.00?

Ⓐ how many miles they have to go

Ⓑ what time of day they are going

Ⓒ how many of them will be going

Ⓓ how many stops the bus will make

GO ON ⇨

Posttest, part 2, page 3

Lesson 10: Problem Solving

Directions Darken the circle by the correct answer to each problem.

15. Last month the students of Wingate School collected 657 empty soda cans for recycling. This month they collected 423 cans. How many cans did they collect for both months?
- Ⓐ 1,000 cans
- Ⓑ 234 cans
- Ⓒ 1,234 cans
- Ⓓ 1,080 cans

16. Willie used a candy thermometer to make fudge. When he began cooking the mixture, it measured 85 degrees. The fudge was done when the temperature reached 235 degrees. By how many degrees did the temperature increase while cooking?
- Ⓐ 150 degrees
- Ⓑ 250 degrees
- Ⓒ 320 degrees
- Ⓓ Not given

17. Shane's hobby is photography. On his last camping trip, he took 2 rolls of 24-exposure film and 3 rolls of 36-exposure film. How many pictures did he take altogether?
- Ⓐ 108 pictures
- Ⓑ 48 pictures
- Ⓒ 156 pictures
- Ⓓ 60 pictures

18. Rudy bought a 36-exposure roll of film for $4.80. It cost him $6 to have the film developed. What was the average cost per picture?
- Ⓐ $6
- Ⓑ 30¢
- Ⓒ 68¢
- Ⓓ 80¢

19. Karla painted a mural that is 8.06 meters long. Her friend Ray painted a mural that is 8.54 meters long. How much longer is Ray's mural than Karla's mural?
- Ⓐ 4.8 meters
- Ⓑ 48 meters
- Ⓒ 0.48 meters
- Ⓓ 4.08 meters

20. Marcella's mother baked muffins and breads for the holiday. She used $1\frac{1}{2}$ pounds of nuts for both recipes. If she used $\frac{3}{4}$ pounds of nuts for the muffins, how much did she use for the bread?
- Ⓐ 1 pound
- Ⓑ $\frac{1}{2}$ pound
- Ⓒ $\frac{1}{4}$ pound
- Ⓓ $\frac{3}{4}$ pound

STOP

Lesson 1: Number Concepts

Directions Darken the circle by the correct answer to each problem.

 **Testing Tips**

1. Read each question carefully to make sure you understand exactly what to do.
2. Study all the choices before you decide on the correct answer.
3. If a pattern is used, think about what would come next in the pattern.

Sample:

What is another way to write
5 thousands 9 tens?

Ⓐ 509
Ⓑ 5,090
Ⓒ 5,900
Ⓓ 5,009

Answer

The correct answer is B. *5,090*. 5 *thousands* means 5,000, and 9 *tens* means 90. *5,090* is the only number that has *5* in the thousands place and *9* in the tens place.

Now Try These *You have 30 minutes.*

1. Which of these numbers has a 4 in the ten-thousands place?
   Ⓐ 367,543
   Ⓑ 4,392
   Ⓒ 4,763,582
   Ⓓ 41,506

2. Which of these is 960?
   Ⓐ 9 + 600
   Ⓑ 900 + 60
   Ⓒ 90 + 60
   Ⓓ 9,000 + 60

3. What is another way to write 4,036?
   Ⓐ 40 + 30 + 60
   Ⓑ 40 + 36
   Ⓒ 400 + 30 + 6
   Ⓓ 4000 + 30 + 6

4. Which of these is equal to 6?
   Ⓐ 1×6
   Ⓑ $6 + 1$
   Ⓒ 6×6
   Ⓓ 0×6

5. Which number is greater than the others?
   Ⓐ 99,999
   Ⓑ 110,123
   Ⓒ 100,000
   Ⓓ 10,000

6. Which number sentence is true?
   Ⓐ 732 < 419
   Ⓑ 8 < 2
   Ⓒ 12 > 15
   Ⓓ 346 < 364

GO ON ⇨

Lesson 1, page 2

7. Which is the Roman numeral for 128?
Ⓐ CVIII
Ⓑ CVXXIII
Ⓒ CXXIIIV
Ⓓ CXXVIII

8. What does the 6 in 36,839 mean?
Ⓐ six thousand
Ⓑ sixty thousand
Ⓒ six hundred
Ⓓ sixty

9. Which is the expanded form of 5,013?
Ⓐ 5,000 + 13
Ⓑ 5,000 + 100 + 3
Ⓒ 5,000 + 10 + 3
Ⓓ 500 + 10 + 3

10. Which of these is an even number?
Ⓐ 38
Ⓑ 29
Ⓒ 75
Ⓓ 63

11. Which number is missing in this pattern?
30, 24, 18, _____, 6
Ⓐ 12
Ⓑ 14
Ⓒ 16
Ⓓ 10

12. Which expression shows 75 as a product of prime factors?
Ⓐ $5 \times 5 \times 3$
Ⓑ 3×25
Ⓒ 15×5
Ⓓ 25^3

13. Which number will correctly complete this number sentence?
$(2 + 7) + 15 = 2 + (\boxed{} + 15)$
Ⓐ 9
Ⓑ 7
Ⓒ 2
Ⓓ 15

14. Which of the following numbers would be a possible remainder when a whole number less than 50 is divided by 3?
Ⓐ 8
Ⓑ 6
Ⓒ 5
Ⓓ 2

15. What is the least common multiple of 3 and 4?
Ⓐ 9
Ⓑ 12
Ⓒ 6
Ⓓ 34

GO ON ⇨

Lesson 1, page 3

16. Which of these sets of numbers is ordered from greatest to least?
- Ⓐ 4,729   2,678   5,270
- Ⓑ 5,270   2,678   4,729
- Ⓒ 5,270   4,729   2,678
- Ⓓ 4,729   5,270   2,678

17. Which numbers complete this number pattern?

30, _____, _____, 12, 6
- Ⓐ 17, 13
- Ⓑ 28, 23
- Ⓒ 24, 18
- Ⓓ 26, 16

18. At a marshmallow-eating contest, the winner ate 20 marshmallows in 5 minutes. At that rate, how many would the winner have eaten if the contest had lasted 25 minutes?
- Ⓐ 25
- Ⓑ 40
- Ⓒ 100
- Ⓓ 120

19. What number would be the 6th number in the pattern?

6, 12, 18, ...
- Ⓐ 28
- Ⓑ 30
- Ⓒ 36
- Ⓓ 48

20. What time is 5 hours after 6:45 P.M.?
- Ⓐ 5:45 P.M.
- Ⓑ 11:45 A.M.
- Ⓒ 11:45 P.M.
- Ⓓ 10:45 P.M.

21. How many dots would be in the 8th figure if this pattern continued?
- Ⓐ 8
- Ⓑ 14
- Ⓒ 25
- Ⓓ 29

22. Mr. Garrett designed a pattern in the rock wall around his garden. He used 2 brown rocks, then 5 gray rocks, then 8 tan rocks, then 3 white rocks. If he continues this pattern, what will be the color of the 35th rock?
- Ⓐ brown
- Ⓑ gray
- Ⓒ tan
- Ⓓ white

23. Which numbers complete the following number pattern?

7, 8, 10, 13, _____, _____
- Ⓐ 14, 16
- Ⓑ 16. 19
- Ⓒ 17, 22
- Ⓓ 20, 25

24. The sum of the first 2 numerals in Max's apartment number is twice the sum of the last 2 numerals. Which of these could be Max's apartment number?
- Ⓐ 842
- Ⓑ 824
- Ⓒ 428
- Ⓓ 248

GO ON ⇨

Lesson 1, page 4

25. How many squares would be in the 6th figure if this pattern continued?
- Ⓐ 12
- Ⓑ 15
- Ⓒ 21
- Ⓓ 28

26. What should be the 7th number in the pattern?

3, 6, 12, 24
- Ⓐ 48
- Ⓑ 98
- Ⓒ 164
- Ⓓ 192

27. Randy uses 4 boards to build 1 step, 10 boards to build 2 steps, and 18 boards to build 3 steps. How many boards would he use to build 5 steps?
- Ⓐ 46
- Ⓑ 40
- Ⓒ 30
- Ⓓ 28

28. Which number has a 7 in the ten thousands place?
- Ⓐ 72,439
- Ⓑ 67,838
- Ⓒ 86,725
- Ⓓ 42,371

29. Which is a true sentence?
- Ⓐ 629,387 > 89,974
- Ⓑ 427,600 < 426,700
- Ⓒ 99,999 > 100,000
- Ⓓ 5,555 < 5,554

30. Round 451 to the nearest hundred.
- Ⓐ 400
- Ⓑ 450
- Ⓒ 500
- Ⓓ 451

Your time: _____

Number right: _____

On this lesson I did _____ because _____

_____ .

I think it would help me to _____ because _____

_____ .

Lesson 2: Whole Number Computation

Directions Darken the circle by the correct answer to each problem.

 Testing Tips

1. Look at the sign to make sure you are doing the correct operation.
2. Estimate the answer.
3. Cross out any choices that must be wrong.
4. Check your work.

Sample:

6)2,412

- Ⓐ 42
- Ⓑ 402
- Ⓒ 403
- Ⓓ 502

Answer

The correct answer is B. *402*. If you multiply *402* by *6*, your answer will be *2,412*, so you know the answer is correct.

Now Try These   *You have 30 minutes.*

1.   3,689
     +   3
- Ⓐ 3,692
- Ⓑ 4,702
- Ⓒ 3,792
- Ⓓ 4,692

2.   628
     × 90
- Ⓐ 56,520
- Ⓑ 56,528
- Ⓒ 718
- Ⓓ 56,922

3.   5)64
- Ⓐ 12 R4
- Ⓑ 2 R14
- Ⓒ 14
- Ⓓ 1 R4

4.   804
     − 326
- Ⓐ 522
- Ⓑ 508
- Ⓒ 478
- Ⓓ 57

5.   5,702
     + 4,817
- Ⓐ 10,509
- Ⓑ 10,619
- Ⓒ 10,519
- Ⓓ 885

6.   938 + 79 + 421 =
- Ⓐ 1,540
- Ⓑ 2,439
- Ⓒ 1,438
- Ⓓ 438

GO ON ⇨

Lesson 2, page 2

7. 613 − 422 =
- (A) 192
- (B) 291
- (C) 181
- (D) 191

8. 6,000
− 3,781
- (A) 2,219
- (B) 2,319
- (C) 2,329
- (D) 9,781

9. 855 − 436 =
- (A) 411
- (B) 519
- (C) 419
- (D) 1,291

10. 45 × 100 =
- (A) 4,000
- (B) 1,500
- (C) 4,500
- (D) 5,400

11. 328
× 43
- (A) 13,120
- (B) 14,004
- (C) 13,401
- (D) 14,104

12. 224
× 105
- (A) 23,520
- (B) 23,502
- (C) 23,052
- (D) 329

13. 336 ÷ 42 =
- (A) 8
- (B) 7 R6
- (C) 9
- (D) 12

14. 33)298
- (A) 9
- (B) 9 R1
- (C) 9 R3
- (D) 13

Your time: _____

Number right: _____

On this lesson I did _____ because _____

_____ .

Name _____   Date _____

Lesson 3: Estimation

Directions Darken the circle by the correct answer to each problem.

 Testing Tips

1. Round up to the nearest ten if a number ends in 5 or more.
2. Round up to the nearest hundred if the tens are 50 or more, and so on.
3. Round numbers when you estimate.
4. Remember that the word about means an exact answer is not needed.

Sample:

Estimate the sum of 179 and 490.

- Ⓐ 679
- Ⓑ 800
- Ⓒ 500
- Ⓓ 700

Answer

The correct answer is D. **700**. **179** is rounded to 200. **490** is rounded to 500. Then add 200 and 500 to get **700**.

Now Try These *You have 10 minutes.*

1. If you rounded 8,723 to the nearest hundred, what would the number be?
- Ⓐ 9,723
- Ⓑ 8,700
- Ⓒ 9,800
- Ⓓ 8,800

2. Estimate the sum of 29, 12, and 38.
- Ⓐ 70
- Ⓑ 60
- Ⓒ 80
- Ⓓ 50

3. Estimate the product of 4 × 28.
- Ⓐ 80
- Ⓑ 120
- Ⓒ 110
- Ⓓ 90

4. Estimate the difference between 6,990 and 1,875.
- Ⓐ 9,000
- Ⓑ 6,000
- Ⓒ 7,000
- Ⓓ 5,000

5. Which numbers should you use to estimate 463 – 221?
- Ⓐ 460 – 220
- Ⓑ 470 – 220
- Ⓒ 470 – 200
- Ⓓ 460 – 200

6. Which of these should you use to estimate 2,106 – 1,481?
- Ⓐ 2,200 – 1,500
- Ⓑ 2,000 – 1,300
- Ⓒ 2,100 – 1,500
- Ⓓ 2,200 – 1,400

GO ON ⇨

Lesson 3, page 2

7. Estimate the sum of 782 and 341.
- Ⓐ 1,200
- Ⓑ 1,100
- Ⓒ 1,110
- Ⓓ 1,010

8. Which numbers should you use to estimate 872 − 419?
- Ⓐ 900 − 500
- Ⓑ 800 − 500
- Ⓒ 800 − 400
- Ⓓ 900 − 400

9. Kia trimmed a Christmas tree by stringing about 671 pieces of popcorn and 793 cranberries on long threads. About how many cranberries and pieces of popcorn did she use altogether?
- Ⓐ 1,300 pieces
- Ⓑ 1,200 pieces
- Ⓒ 1,500 pieces
- Ⓓ 1,100 pieces

10. Juan can throw a football 42 yards. He can throw a baseball 109 yards. About how much farther can he throw a baseball than a football?
- Ⓐ 70 yards
- Ⓑ 80 yards
- Ⓒ 100 yards
- Ⓓ 150 yards

11. The closest estimate of 3,819 + 5,924 is _____ .
- Ⓐ 8,000
- Ⓑ 9,000
- Ⓒ 10,000
- Ⓓ 11,000

12. Mr. Hobson received 60 applications for the job of clerk in his store. He read 18 applications on Monday, 11 on Tuesday, and 9 on Wednesday. Which is the best estimate of the number of applications left to read?
- Ⓐ fewer than 15
- Ⓑ between 20 and 30
- Ⓒ between 30 and 40
- Ⓓ between 40 and 50

13. The closest estimate of 750 ÷ 8 is _____ .
- Ⓐ 9
- Ⓑ 90
- Ⓒ 900
- Ⓓ 9,000

14. The closest estimate of $17.78 × 12 is _____ .
- Ⓐ $120
- Ⓑ $150
- Ⓒ $170
- Ⓓ $200

Your time: _____

Number right: _____

On this lesson I did _____ because _____

_____ .

Lesson 4: Fractions and Decimals

Directions Darken the circle by the correct answer to each problem.

 Testing Tips

1. A fraction is a part of a whole.
2. Equivalent fractions name the same amount.
3. Divide both terms of a fraction by a common number to find the lowest term of the fraction.
4. Remember that you can add a zero at the end of a decimal number without changing its value.
5. Keep the decimal points in line when you are working with decimal problems.

Sample A:

$\frac{5}{6}$ is equivalent to _____ .

Ⓐ $\frac{5}{10}$

Ⓑ $\frac{10}{12}$

Ⓒ $\frac{5}{12}$

Ⓓ $\frac{1}{10}$

Answer

In Sample A, the correct answer is B. *10/12*. Both fractions name equivalent amounts.

Sample B:

$$\begin{array}{r} 0.86 \\ + 0.25 \\ \hline \end{array}$$

Ⓐ 1.01

Ⓑ 1.11

Ⓒ 1.10

Ⓓ 1.010

Answer

In Sample B, the correct answer is B. *1.11*. Adding and regrouping decimals is like adding and regrouping whole numbers.

Now Try These *You have 30 minutes.*

1. Which is true?

Ⓐ $\frac{1}{4} > \frac{1}{3}$

Ⓑ $\frac{4}{7} < \frac{2}{5}$

Ⓒ $\frac{2}{9} > \frac{1}{3}$

Ⓓ $\frac{7}{10} > \frac{4}{15}$

2. Which number renames $\frac{17}{8}$?

Ⓐ $2\frac{1}{8}$

Ⓑ 3

Ⓒ $2\frac{5}{8}$

Ⓓ 2

GO ON ⇨

Lesson 4, page 2

3. Which is the lowest term for $\frac{5}{25}$?

Ⓐ $\frac{1}{4}$

Ⓑ $\frac{1}{4}$

Ⓒ $\frac{5}{10}$

Ⓓ $\frac{1}{5}$

4. What fraction shows how many of this group are <u>not</u> shaded?

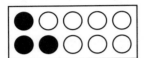

Ⓐ $\frac{3}{10}$

Ⓑ $\frac{7}{3}$

Ⓒ $\frac{7}{10}$

Ⓓ $\frac{3}{7}$

5. $\frac{3}{4} \times 8 =$

Ⓐ $4\frac{1}{2}$

Ⓑ 6

Ⓒ $2\frac{4}{8}$

Ⓓ 11

6. What is the lowest term for the answer to $\frac{3}{4} - \frac{3}{20}$?

Ⓐ $\frac{3}{5}$

Ⓑ $\frac{18}{20}$

Ⓒ $\frac{6}{20}$

Ⓓ $\frac{6}{24}$

7. $\frac{5}{9} + \frac{1}{3} =$

Ⓐ $\frac{4}{6}$

Ⓑ $\frac{4}{9}$

Ⓒ $\frac{5}{27}$

Ⓓ $\frac{8}{9}$

8. $9\frac{1}{3} \times \frac{2}{6} =$

Ⓐ $2\frac{2}{9}$

Ⓑ $3\frac{2}{9}$

Ⓒ $3\frac{1}{8}$

Ⓓ $3\frac{1}{9}$

9. $\frac{2}{5} \times$ _____ $= 10$

Ⓐ 50

Ⓑ 25

Ⓒ 35

Ⓓ 4

10. $\frac{7}{12} \div \frac{1}{6} =$

Ⓐ $3\frac{1}{2}$

Ⓑ $2\frac{3}{4}$

Ⓒ $3\frac{1}{4}$

Ⓓ $\frac{7}{72}$

11. Which mixed number does the picture stand for?

Ⓐ $3\frac{6}{8}$

Ⓑ $3\frac{1}{8}$

Ⓒ $4\frac{1}{8}$

Ⓓ $4\frac{7}{8}$

12. George ate $\frac{1}{3}$ of a pizza. His friend Jack ate $\frac{1}{6}$ of the pizza. How much of the pizza was eaten?

Ⓐ $\frac{2}{6}$ pizza

Ⓑ $\frac{2}{3}$ pizza

Ⓒ $\frac{1}{2}$ pizza

Ⓓ $\frac{2}{9}$ pizza

GO ON ⇨

Lesson 4, page 3

13. $26.07
    + $39.81

Ⓐ $65.88
Ⓑ $66.07
Ⓒ $76.77
Ⓓ Not given

14. 93.11 − 44.07 =
Ⓐ 47.06
Ⓑ 49.04
Ⓒ 59.18
Ⓓ Not given

15. 65.09
    + 82.35

Ⓐ 147.35
Ⓑ 147.44
Ⓒ 147.64
Ⓓ 157.35

16. $33.21 − $11.82 =
Ⓐ $22.49
Ⓑ $22.38
Ⓒ $21.39
Ⓓ $21.49

17. 5.27
    × 7.8

Ⓐ 41.106
Ⓑ 42.106
Ⓒ 41.116
Ⓓ 57.35

18. $73.18
    × 6.00

Ⓐ $439.08
Ⓑ $430.80
Ⓒ $420.80
Ⓓ $79.18

19. 6.517 ÷ 7 =
Ⓐ 0.931
Ⓑ 93.1
Ⓒ 9.31
Ⓓ 45.619

20. 9)‾34.29
Ⓐ 38.1
Ⓑ 3.81
Ⓒ 0.381
Ⓓ 25.29

21. Theresa had a $20 bill. She bought some construction paper for $3.10 and a bottle of glue for $1.95. How much change should she receive?
Ⓐ $17.95
Ⓑ $14.95
Ⓒ $8.05
Ⓓ $3.15

GO ON ⇨

Lesson 4, page 4

22. Which number sentence is true?
- Ⓐ 5.8 = 5.80
- Ⓑ 5.8 > 5.80
- Ⓒ 5.8 < 5.80
- Ⓓ 5.80 > 5.8

23. 0.52 + 0.96 =
- Ⓐ 14.80
- Ⓑ 2.48
- Ⓒ 1.40
- Ⓓ 1.48

24. 947 ÷ 100 =
- Ⓐ 94.7
- Ⓑ 94.07
- Ⓒ .0947
- Ⓓ 9.47

25. $315.50
  × 8
- Ⓐ $2,423.00
- Ⓑ $2,524.80
- Ⓒ $2,524.00
- Ⓓ $323.50

26. Round 35.642 to the nearest tenth.
- Ⓐ 36.042
- Ⓑ 35.6
- Ⓒ 35.7
- Ⓓ 36

27. Wendy and Ronnie are planning a bicycle trip to a town that is 49.62 kilometers from their home. They are planning to take 3 days for the trip. How many kilometers must they travel each day?
- Ⓐ 15
- Ⓑ 12
- Ⓒ 9.00
- Ⓓ 16.54

28. Which of these is equal to $0.95?
- Ⓐ 2 quarters, 5 nickels, 1 dime
- Ⓑ 3 quarters, 1 dime, 1 nickel
- Ⓒ 2 quarters, 4 dimes, 1 nickel
- Ⓓ 3 quarters, 3 dimes, 3 nickels

29. 18)8.28
- Ⓐ 0.46
- Ⓑ 4.6
- Ⓒ 46
- Ⓓ 26.28

 STOP

Your time: _____

Number right: _____

On this lesson I did _____ because _____

_____.

Name _____ Date _____

Lesson 5: Ratios and Percents

Directions Darken the circle for the correct answer.

Testing Tips

1. The ratio of any number to 100 is called a percent.
2. Ratios can be written as a fraction or as a percent (%).
3. A decimal can be changed to a percent by moving the decimal point to the right two digits.

Sample:

Write 16 to 100 as a ratio and as a percent.

Ⓐ $\frac{16}{16}$, 16%
Ⓑ $\frac{16}{100}$, 16%
Ⓒ $\frac{100}{15}$, 100%
Ⓓ $\frac{100}{16}$, 100%

Answer

The correct answer is B. $\frac{16}{100}$, *16%*. Both the fraction and the percent tell about 16 being part of 100.

Now Try These *You have 20 minutes.*

1. Four out of 5 students bring their lunch from home. 50% of the students who bring their lunch buy dessert at school. What ratio of the students bring their lunch and buy dessert at school?
   Ⓐ 4 out of 5
   Ⓑ 1 out of 4
   Ⓒ 2 out of 5
   Ⓓ 1 out of 5

2. 125 : 100 = 75 : ?
   Ⓐ 10
   Ⓑ 15
   Ⓒ 60
   Ⓓ 25

3. Hector and Justin played cards. Hector won 6 out of 8 games. What percent of the games did Justin win?
   Ⓐ 40%
   Ⓑ 25%
   Ⓒ 75%
   Ⓓ 60%

4. 7 : 8 = 14 : ?
   Ⓐ 16
   Ⓑ 20
   Ⓒ 17
   Ⓓ 13

GO ON ⇨

Lesson 5, page 2

5. Which fraction shows the ratio of 17 to 15?

   Ⓐ $\frac{17}{15}$

   Ⓑ $\frac{15}{17}$

   Ⓒ $1\frac{2}{15}$

   Ⓓ $\frac{17}{25}$

6. Which pair of ratios is equal?

   Ⓐ $\frac{27}{54}$, $\frac{9}{18}$

   Ⓑ $\frac{12}{5}$, $\frac{4}{25}$

   Ⓒ $\frac{6}{12}$, $\frac{1}{12}$

   Ⓓ $\frac{7}{4}$, $\frac{35}{8}$

7. Which percent is the same as the ratio 89:100?

   Ⓐ 90%

   Ⓑ 89%

   Ⓒ 100%

   Ⓓ 11%

8. Change 2% to a decimal.

   Ⓐ 0.02

   Ⓑ 2.0

   Ⓒ 0.2

   Ⓓ 20.00

9. Change $\frac{9}{25}$ to a percent.

   Ⓐ 25%

   Ⓑ 90%

   Ⓒ 36%

   Ⓓ 10%

10. What percent of this circle is shaded?

   Ⓐ 40%

   Ⓑ 60%

   Ⓒ 30%

   Ⓓ 50%

11. Find 50% of 92.

   Ⓐ 50

   Ⓑ 46

   Ⓒ 54

   Ⓓ 44

12. Find 39% of 47 using a decimal.

   Ⓐ 1.833

   Ⓑ 18.33

   Ⓒ 183.3

   Ⓓ 1.083

13. If sales tax is 5%, what is the tax on $12.90?

   Ⓐ 65¢

   Ⓑ 32¢

   Ⓒ 48¢

   Ⓓ 82¢

14. Use 25% to estimate 27% of 88.

   Ⓐ 45

   Ⓑ 36

   Ⓒ 22

   Ⓓ 25

Your time: _____

Number right: _____

On this lesson I did _____ because _____

_____.

Lesson 6: Measurement and Geometry

Directions Darken the circle by the correct answer to each problem.

⭐ **Testing Tips**

1. Study the information given about each measurement before you answer the question.
2. Be sure to choose the correct unit of measurement to solve the problem.
3. Look for key words such as **length, mass, weight, and metric** to help you choose your answer.
4. Perimeter is the measurement around the outside of a shape.
5. Area is the number of square units inside a shape.
6. Volume is the number of cubic units inside a shape.

Sample:

What is the area of the square in this diagram?

Ⓐ 36 sq m
Ⓑ 72 sq m
Ⓒ 81 sq m
Ⓓ 182 sq m

9 m

Answer

The correct answer is C. **81 sq m.** To find the area covered by a space, multiply the length by the width. In a square, all sides are equal. By multiplying 9 x 9, we get an area of **81 sq m.**

🕐 **Now Try These** *You have 30 minutes.*

1. What is the volume?

Ⓐ 36 cu in.
Ⓑ 13 cu in.
Ⓒ 64 cu in.
Ⓓ 52 cu in.

4 inches
4 inches
4 inches

2. What is the perimeter of a garden plot that is shaped like this?

Ⓐ 114 m
Ⓑ 105 m
Ⓒ 125 m
Ⓓ 135 m

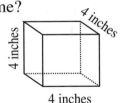

27 m
30 m

3. Which of these is usually sold by the yard?

Ⓐ eggs
Ⓑ cloth
Ⓒ cheese
Ⓓ milk

4. Which of these is usually sold by the liter?

Ⓐ potatoes
Ⓑ cookies
Ⓒ milk
Ⓓ paper

GO ON ⇨

Lesson 6, page 2

5. Which of these represents the greatest distance?
- Ⓐ 2 kilometers
- Ⓑ 10 meters
- Ⓒ 100 centimeters
- Ⓓ 1000 millimeters

6. Which of the following metric units of measurement is best to use to measure the length of a room?
- Ⓐ meter
- Ⓑ liter
- Ⓒ centimeter
- Ⓓ kilogram

7. Karl uses 2 cups of cocoa in his special recipe for chocolate fudge cake. How many ounces of cocoa is Karl using in his recipe?
- Ⓐ 4
- Ⓑ 8
- Ⓒ 12
- Ⓓ 16

8. One yard is closest in value to which of the following measurements?
- Ⓐ 1 kilogram
- Ⓑ 1 quart
- Ⓒ 1 liter
- Ⓓ 1 meter

9. 4 quarts =
- Ⓐ 1 pint
- Ⓑ 1 cup
- Ⓒ 1 gallon
- Ⓓ 1 pound

10. Which of the following units of measurement is best to use to describe the weight of a box of breakfast cereal?
- Ⓐ feet
- Ⓑ ounces
- Ⓒ liters
- Ⓓ inches

11. 100 centimeters =
- Ⓐ 1 yard
- Ⓑ 1 liter
- Ⓒ 1 meter
- Ⓓ 1 kilometer

12. The diagram below shows the playground at Meili's school. What is the perimeter of the playground?
- Ⓐ 105 m
- Ⓑ 114 m
- Ⓒ 124 m
- Ⓓ 135 m

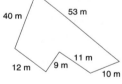

13. Maggie wanted to sew a new tablecloth for her round dining table. The radius of the table is 19 inches. What is the diameter of the table?
- Ⓐ 9½ inches
- Ⓑ 28 inches
- Ⓒ 38 inches
- Ⓓ 57 inches

GO ON ⇨

Lesson 6, page 3

14. Which of these is a radius?

Ⓐ AB
Ⓑ CD
Ⓒ BD
Ⓓ AD

15. Which of these is a chord?

Ⓐ AX
Ⓑ AB
Ⓒ BX
Ⓓ CX

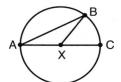

16. What is the perimeter of this figure?

Ⓐ 24 cm
Ⓑ 12 cm
Ⓒ 36 cm
Ⓓ 39 cm

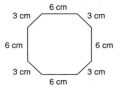

17. Which is the name of a triangle that has no congruent sides?

Ⓐ isosceles triangle
Ⓑ scalene triangle
Ⓒ equilateral triangle
Ⓓ right triangle

18. What is the temperature on this thermometer?

Ⓐ 45°
Ⓑ 39°
Ⓒ 41°
Ⓓ 36°

19. Which angle is an acute angle?

20. Which one of these is not a quadrilateral?

Ⓐ circle
Ⓑ rhombus
Ⓒ parallelogram
Ⓓ trapezoid

21. Which of the following pairs of lines is perpendicular?

22. Which point shows where these lines intersect?

Ⓐ J
Ⓑ K
Ⓒ L
Ⓓ M

23. Which shape is a cylinder?

GO ON ⇨

Lesson 6, page 4

24. Which of the following shows a line segment that is drawn and labeled in the figure?

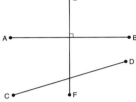

- Ⓐ $\overline{AE}$
- Ⓑ $\overline{AB}$
- Ⓒ $\overline{BD}$
- Ⓓ $\overline{FD}$

25. What is the area of the square shown here?

- Ⓐ 32 m²
- Ⓑ 64 m²
- Ⓒ 96 m²
- Ⓓ 256 m²

8 m

26. What is the length of the diameter in the circle shown here?

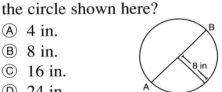

- Ⓐ 4 in.
- Ⓑ 8 in.
- Ⓒ 16 in.
- Ⓓ 24 in.

27. Which clock shows that the time is 6:45?

A   B

C   D

- Ⓐ A
- Ⓑ B
- Ⓒ C
- Ⓓ D

28. Which of these figures shows a line of symmetry?

A   B   C   D

- Ⓐ A
- Ⓑ B
- Ⓒ C
- Ⓓ D

29. 5,280 feet =

- Ⓐ 1 meter
- Ⓑ 1 mile
- Ⓒ 1 kilometer
- Ⓓ 1 kilogram

STOP

Your time: _____

Number right: _____

On this lesson I did _____ because _____

_____ .

Name _____ Date _____

Lesson 7: Statistics and Probability

Directions Darken the circle by the correct answer to each problem.

**Testing Tips**

1. A pictograph uses pictures to show information.
2. A circle graph uses slices of a circle to show information.
3. A bar graph uses bars to show information.
4. A line graph uses lines on a grid to show information.
5. All graphs have a title and a scale to show amounts. They also have categories to tell what information is being shown.
6. First, study the graph carefully. Then, notice the title. Finally, study the scale and use your finger to point to each piece of information.
7. Look for key words or numbers in the question that tell you what to look for in the graph.
8. Probability is the chance that something will probably happen. The outcome is the result of the activity or event.
9. You can predict the chance that something will happen by using what you observe.
10. When there is more of something in a group or on a spinner, the probability is greater that part will be chosen.

Sample:

In what year did it snow the most?
- Ⓐ 1995
- Ⓑ 1994
- Ⓒ 1993
- Ⓓ 1992

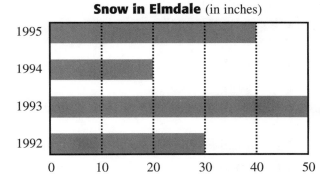

Snow in Elmdale (in inches)

Answer

The correct answer is C. *1993*.

Now Try These *You have 30 minutes.*

Use the graph above to answer questions 1–2.

1. How many inches in all did it snow in 1994 and 1995?
- Ⓐ 20
- Ⓑ 40
- Ⓒ 70
- Ⓓ 60

2. In what year did it snow 30 inches?
- Ⓐ 1995
- Ⓑ 1992
- Ⓒ 1993
- Ⓓ 1994

GO ON ⇨

Lesson 7, page 2

Use this graph to answer questions 3–4.

Favorite Subject for Fifth-Grade Students

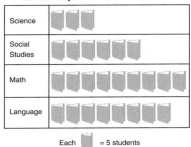

Each [book] = 5 students

Use this graph to answer questions 6–8.

TYPES OF BOOKS READ

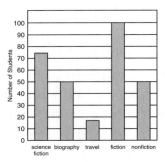

3. How many students chose language as their favorite subject?
- Ⓐ 40 students
- Ⓑ 8 students
- Ⓒ 20 students
- Ⓓ 50 students

4. How many more students like math better than science?
- Ⓐ 45 students
- Ⓑ 15 students
- Ⓒ 30 students
- Ⓓ 25 students

5. Look at the circle graph. What percent of his money does Miguel spend on lunch out and magazines?

MIGUEL'S EARNINGS

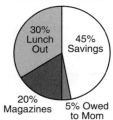

- Ⓐ 45%
- Ⓑ 50%
- Ⓒ 5%
- Ⓓ 25%

6. Which 2 categories of books were read by the same number of students?
- Ⓐ science fiction and biography
- Ⓑ travel and nonfiction
- Ⓒ biography and nonfiction
- Ⓓ fiction and science fiction

7. How many students read books on travel?
- Ⓐ 10 students
- Ⓑ 18 students
- Ⓒ 20 students
- Ⓓ 30 students

8. Which category of books was read by the most students?
- Ⓐ fiction
- Ⓑ science fiction
- Ⓒ biography
- Ⓓ nonfiction

9. A graph used to show changes by connecting dots is called _____ .
- Ⓐ a pictograph
- Ⓑ a circle graph
- Ⓒ a bar graph
- Ⓓ a line graph

GO ON ⇨

Lesson 7, page 3

The graph shows how many hours Lena baby-sat last week. Study the graph. Then answer questions 10–13.

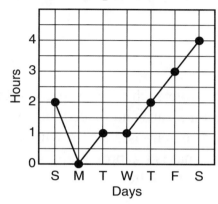

10. On which day did Lena baby-sit for 3 hours?
- Ⓐ Friday
- Ⓑ Sunday
- Ⓒ Thursday
- Ⓓ Saturday

11. On which day did Lena baby-sit the most hours?
- Ⓐ Sunday
- Ⓑ Thursday
- Ⓒ Saturday
- Ⓓ Monday

12. On which day did Lena not baby-sit?
- Ⓐ Saturday
- Ⓑ Wednesday
- Ⓒ Tuesday
- Ⓓ Monday

13. How many hours did Lena baby-sit during this week?
- Ⓐ 4 hours
- Ⓑ 6 hours
- Ⓒ 13 hours
- Ⓓ 16 hours

14. In a total of 10 spins, which number will the spinner probably point to the greatest number of times?
- Ⓐ 1
- Ⓑ 2
- Ⓒ 4
- Ⓓ 5

15. There are 4 red beads, 8 yellow beads, and 2 pink beads in a container. If 1 bead is picked at random from the container, what are the chances it will be red?
- Ⓐ $\frac{2}{14}$
- Ⓑ $\frac{4}{14}$
- Ⓒ $\frac{6}{14}$
- Ⓓ $\frac{8}{14}$

Answer questions 16–18 about the cards.

16. What is the probability of choosing a card with the letter *A*?
- Ⓐ $\frac{8}{10}$
- Ⓑ $\frac{1}{5}$
- Ⓒ $\frac{2}{5}$
- Ⓓ $\frac{4}{5}$

17. What is the probability of choosing a card with the letter *C*?
- Ⓐ $\frac{9}{10}$
- Ⓑ $\frac{7}{10}$
- Ⓒ $\frac{3}{10}$
- Ⓓ $\frac{1}{10}$

18. What is the probability of choosing a card with the letter *D*?
- Ⓐ $\frac{1}{2}$
- Ⓑ $\frac{2}{5}$
- Ⓒ $\frac{3}{5}$
- Ⓓ $\frac{2}{3}$

GO ON ⇨

Lesson 7, page 4

Answer questions 19–22 based on a cube that has faces numbered 1–6.

19. What is the probability of the cube landing on an even number?

Ⓐ 1:2
Ⓑ 2:1
Ⓒ 6:2
Ⓓ 2:6

20. What is the probability of the cube landing on an odd number?

Ⓐ 3:5
Ⓑ 5:6
Ⓒ 1:2
Ⓓ 2:3

21. What is the probability of the cube landing on a prime number?

Ⓐ 0
Ⓑ 2:3
Ⓒ 1:2
Ⓓ 1:3

22. What is the probability of the cube landing on a number less than 4?

Ⓐ $\frac{1}{3}$
Ⓑ $\frac{1}{2}$
Ⓒ $\frac{1}{6}$
Ⓓ $\frac{3}{6}$

23. Kareem wrote each letter of the word *average* on a card and placed the cards in a hat. If he chooses a card without looking, what is the probability that he will choose the letter *r*?

Ⓐ $\frac{2}{7}$
Ⓑ $\frac{1}{6}$
Ⓒ $\frac{1}{7}$
Ⓓ $\frac{1}{14}$

24. It is Carmela's turn in a board game she is playing with her family. What is the probability that Carmela will lose a turn on this spin?

Ⓐ $\frac{1}{8}$
Ⓑ $\frac{2}{8}$
Ⓒ $\frac{3}{8}$
Ⓓ $\frac{5}{8}$

STOP

Your time: _____

Number right: _____

On this lesson I did _____ because _____

_____.

Name _____ Date _____

Lesson 8: Pre-Algebra

Directions Darken the circle by the correct answer to each problem.

Testing Tips

1. Algebra expressions use letters and symbols to represent numbers. These letters and symbols are called variables.
2. A variable holds a place for a number. You can use a variable to represent a number. For example, $n - 4$ means 4 less than a number represented by n.

Sample:

If $y + 13 = 25$, then $y =$

- Ⓐ 6
- Ⓑ 12
- Ⓒ 15
- Ⓓ 38

Answer

The correct answer is B. **12**. Subtract 13 from both sides of the equation, and $y = 25 - 13 = 12$.

Now Try These   *You have 15 minutes.*

1. If $25 - y = 18$, what is the value of y?
- Ⓐ 4
- Ⓑ 7
- Ⓒ 18
- Ⓓ 43

2. If $x = 4$, then $x + 5 =$
- Ⓐ 1
- Ⓑ 8
- Ⓒ 10
- Ⓓ 9

3. If $x - 296 = 412$, then $x =$
- Ⓐ 116
- Ⓑ 708
- Ⓒ 4,252
- Ⓓ 121,952

4. If $500 - x = 280$, then $x =$
- Ⓐ 780
- Ⓑ 520
- Ⓒ 220
- Ⓓ 200

5. If $36 \div x = 6$, what is the value of x?
- Ⓐ 2
- Ⓑ 3
- Ⓒ 6
- Ⓓ 9

6. If $y - 200 = 180$, then $y =$
- Ⓐ 380
- Ⓑ 320
- Ⓒ 280
- Ⓓ 220

GO ON ⇨

Lesson 8, page 2

7. If y = 54, then y ÷ 9 =
- (A) 63
- (B) 45
- (C) 12
- (D) 6

8. If y = 9, then y − 4 =
- (A) 36
- (B) 13
- (C) 12
- (D) 5

9. If y − 225 = 570, then y =
- (A) 35
- (B) 235
- (C) 395
- (D) 795

10. If x = 36, then x ÷ 9 =
- (A) 3
- (B) 4
- (C) 27
- (D) 45

11. If 125 + x = 550, what is the value of x?
- (A) 225
- (B) 275
- (C) 375
- (D) 425

12. If x = 6, then x + 9 =
- (A) 1
- (B) 10
- (C) 15
- (D) 18

13. If 30 − y = 22, what is the value of y?
- (A) 52
- (B) 28
- (C) 12
- (D) 8

14. If y = 32, then y ÷ 8 =
- (A) 40
- (B) 32
- (C) 6
- (D) 4

Your time: _____

Number right: _____

On this lesson I did _____ because _____.

I think it would help me to _____ because _____.

Lesson 9: Problem-Solving Strategies

Directions Darken the circle by the best strategy to solve each problem.

 **Testing Tips**

1. Read each problem carefully.
2. Find the main idea.
3. Think about important details and information.
4. Decide whether you have chosen the best strategy.

Sample:

The Packard School bookstore sold school pennants for a fund-raiser. On Monday they sold 60 pennants for $2.50 each. On Tuesday they sold 52 pennants for $2.00 each. On Wednesday they sold 75 pennants for $1.50 each. On Thursday they sold 58 pennants for $1.00 each. Which strategy would you use to compare the money earned in the 4 days and to find the total amount of money they made?

Ⓐ find a pattern
Ⓑ make a table
Ⓒ use logic
Ⓓ use estimation

Answer

The correct answer is B. ***make a table***. Making a table is the best way to organize this information to solve the problem.

Now Try These *You have 25 minutes.*

1. The Eatwell Diner used 232 pounds of vegetables in 1 week. The next week they used 292 pounds of vegetables. About how many pounds of vegetables were used in these 2 weeks?
   Ⓐ work backwards
   Ⓑ make a table
   Ⓒ use estimation
   Ⓓ use logic

2. Dan has 6 coins. They are worth $0.67. Which coins does Dan have?
   Ⓐ make a list
   Ⓑ guess and check
   Ⓒ make a graph
   Ⓓ find the pattern

GO ON ⇨

Lesson 9, page 2

3. Mindy is baking cookies for her friend's party. She is baking chocolate cookies and sugar cookies. She wants to decorate the tops of the cookies with either chocolate chips or walnut halves. How many different combinations can she make?

Ⓐ make a list
Ⓑ use logic
Ⓒ choose an operation
Ⓓ guess and check

4. Ten students ran in the 100-meter relay race. Fourteen students ran in the 200-meter relay race. Seven students ran in both races. How many students ran in only 1 of the races?

Ⓐ estimation
Ⓑ make a graph
Ⓒ work backwards
Ⓓ use logic

5. Wanda is saving her money for a trip next summer. By the end of last week, she had saved $76. She had earned $35 for baby-sitting. Yesterday she bought a new T-shirt for $15. How much money did she have in her savings before last week?

Ⓐ identify extra information
Ⓑ choose an operation
Ⓒ make a chart
Ⓓ work backwards

6. Dale is planning to make gifts for his family. He needs to buy craft supplies for all the gifts. He spent $5 for yarn the first day he went shopping, $8 for beads the next day, and $6 for ribbons on the third day. If he continues to spend money this way, about how much will he spend in a week?

Ⓐ make a table
Ⓑ find a pattern
Ⓒ make a graph
Ⓓ choose the operation

7. Gemella bought a blouse as a gift for Sonia. She is sharing the cost of the gift with her friend Rosie. She can't find the receipt, so she doesn't know exactly how much Rosie owes her. She knows that she paid for the blouse with a $20 bill. What else does she need to know in order to know exactly how much money she spent?

Ⓐ the color of the blouse
Ⓑ how much change she received
Ⓒ the name of the store
Ⓓ the size of the blouse

8. Andy has 62 baseball cards and 96 football cards. Marty has 143 baseball cards and 79 football cards. How many baseball cards do Andy and Marty have altogether?

Ⓐ guess and check
Ⓑ identify extra information
Ⓒ work backwards
Ⓓ make a list

GO ON ⇨

Lesson 9, page 3

9. Yoko, Ivy, and Lynda planned to meet at the library after school. One girl walked, 1 rode her bike, and the other skated. Lynda doesn't know how to skate. Ivy waved from her bike when she saw Lynda crossing the street. How did each girl get to the library?

Ⓐ make a list
Ⓑ use estimation
Ⓒ use logic
Ⓓ choose an operation

10. The students in Longfellow School have decided to take part in their town's food drive. Their goal is to collect 600 cans of food. Each student plans to collect 5 cans. What do you need to know to find out whether the students will be able to reach their goal?

Ⓐ how many people will provide food
Ⓑ how many students there are at Longfellow School
Ⓒ how many grocery stores there are
Ⓓ how much each can costs

11. Wanda is trying to decide what to wear to school tomorrow. She has 3 pairs of jeans, 4 tops, and 2 pairs of shoes to choose from. How many different clothing combinations does Wanda have?

Ⓐ 24
Ⓑ 14
Ⓒ 12
Ⓓ 9

12. Manuel and his friends are giving out flyers for a local supermarket. They have 1,000 flyers to give out. They plan to divide the flyers into stacks containing 50 flyers each. To find how many stacks each person will have, what do you need to know?

Ⓐ how many houses they will have to go to
Ⓑ how many friends will be distributing the flyers
Ⓒ what street they will go to
Ⓓ where the local supermarket is located

13. Kenny baby-sat for his sister Katherine's 2 small children 3.5 hours each day after school this week and 5 hours on Saturday. Which sentence could be used to find how many more hours he baby-sat after school than on Saturday?

Ⓐ $5 - 3.5 = \boxed{}$
Ⓑ $(5 \times 3.5) + 5 = \boxed{}$
Ⓒ $(5 \times 3.5) - 5 = \boxed{}$
Ⓓ $(5 \times 5) - 3.5 = \boxed{}$

14. Each rack at the neighborhood bowling alley holds 24 bowling balls. There are 4 racks on each of 3 walls. What number sentence could be used to find the total number of bowling balls in the racks when they are full?

Ⓐ $24 \times 4 \times 3 = \boxed{}$
Ⓑ $(24 \div 4) \times 3 = \boxed{}$
Ⓒ $(24 + 4) \times 3 = \boxed{}$
Ⓓ $4 \times (24 + 3) = \boxed{}$

GO ON ⇨

Lesson 9, page 4

15. How much would it cost to carpet a room that is 18 feet long and 15 feet wide if the carpet costs $18.50 a square yard?
What strategy should you use to solve this problem?
- Ⓐ guess and check
- Ⓑ choose the operation
- Ⓒ use a multi-step plan
- Ⓓ make a graph

16. Tara baby-sat 3 hours on Tuesday afternoon and 4 hours on Friday afternoon. Next week she hopes to baby-sit at least 10 hours. How many hours in all did she baby-sit on Tuesday and Friday?
- Ⓐ identify extra information
- Ⓑ too little information
- Ⓒ make a list
- Ⓓ make a table

17. Chang is designing a tabletop made of small tile squares. He has red tiles, blue tiles, and black tiles. He will also use small, round white and gold tiles for the design. How many different ways can he combine these tiles?
- Ⓐ estimation
- Ⓑ choose an operation
- Ⓒ work backwards
- Ⓓ make a list

18. Leonard has $38 to spend on CDs and tapes. The tapes he wants cost $7.78 each. The CDs cost $9.98. Does he have enough money to buy 3 tapes and 2 CDs?
- Ⓐ use estimation
- Ⓑ work backwards
- Ⓒ use logic
- Ⓓ make a list

19. Andy is saving his money to buy new in-line skates. He saved $2 the first month, $5 the second month, $8 the third month, and $11 the fourth month. If he continues this way, how much money will he save in 6 months?
- Ⓐ find a pattern
- Ⓑ use guess and check
- Ⓒ choose an operation
- Ⓓ use logic

20. Toby bought supplies for her birthday party. She spent $7.95 for hats and $6.45 for party baskets. If she received $5.60 in change, how much money did she give the clerk?
- Ⓐ make a table
- Ⓑ estimation
- Ⓒ work backwards
- Ⓓ make a list

STOP

Your time: _____

Number right: _____

On this lesson I did _____ because _____

_____ .

Name _____ Date _____

Lesson 10: Problem Solving

Directions Darken the circle by the correct answer to each problem.

 **Testing Tips**

1. Read the problem to find the main idea and the important details.
2. Decide which problem-solving strategy to use. Decide if you need to add, subtract, multiply, or divide. Then work the problem on scratch paper.

Sample:

Eric is in charge of buying the hot dogs for the fifth grade picnic. He will buy 2 hot dogs for each student. There are 64 students in the fifth grade. How many hot dogs should Eric buy?

Ⓐ 100 hot dogs
Ⓑ 64 hot dogs
Ⓒ 128 hot dogs
Ⓓ 66 hot dogs

Answer

The correct answer is C. **128 hot dogs**. To solve the problem, multiply 64 students by 2 hot dogs.

Now Try These *You have 30 minutes.*

1. There are 56 fifth-grade students in your school. If the fifth and sixth grades are divided into 5 classrooms, each with 28 students, how many sixth-grade students are there?
   Ⓐ 112 students
   Ⓑ 74 students
   Ⓒ 84 students
   Ⓓ 56 students

2. Josie, Sergio, and Dorrie were in a marathon. Josie ran 3.25 miles more than Sergio. Sergio ran half as far as Dorrie. Dorrie ran 15 miles. How far did Josie run?
   Ⓐ 10.75 miles
   Ⓑ 18.25 miles
   Ⓒ 11.75 miles
   Ⓓ 16.25 miles

3. Chloe took 3 rolls of film on a trip. Each roll is 24 pictures. If she gives half her pictures to her friends, how many will she have left?
   Ⓐ 72
   Ⓑ 24
   Ⓒ 48
   Ⓓ 36

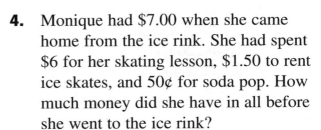

4. Monique had $7.00 when she came home from the ice rink. She had spent $6 for her skating lesson, $1.50 to rent ice skates, and 50¢ for soda pop. How much money did she have in all before she went to the ice rink?
   Ⓐ $15.00
   Ⓑ $8.00
   Ⓒ $13.50
   Ⓓ $9.00

 GO ON ⇨

Lesson 10, page 2

5. Henry is in charge of serving punch at the school picnic. Each punch cup holds 245 milliliters. He needs to fill 14 punch cups. How much punch will he need?

Ⓐ 3,430 milliliters
Ⓑ 825 milliliters
Ⓒ 3,043 milliliters
Ⓓ 4,303 milliliters

6. Maria decorated a tree in her yard with popcorn for birds to eat. On the 1st branch, she hung a string with 4 pieces of popcorn. On the 2nd branch, she hung a string with 8, and on the 3rd branch a string with 16. If she continued this pattern, how many pieces of popcorn would be on the string hung on the 5th branch?

Ⓐ 18
Ⓑ 24
Ⓒ 32
Ⓓ 64

7. Three students have birthdays in the same month. Anthony's birthday is 20 days before Angela's. Angela's birthday is 7 days after Vince's. Vince's birthday is on the 20th. When is Anthony's birthday?

Ⓐ on the 7th
Ⓑ on the 14th
Ⓒ on the 20th
Ⓓ on the 27th

8. A number is more than 645 and when rounded to the nearest hundred is 600. Which of these is the number?

Ⓐ 648
Ⓑ 720
Ⓒ 597
Ⓓ 662

9. Anita wants to earn money to pay for her class trip in the spring. She plans to sell chocolate chip cookies. It costs her $2.10 to make 1 dozen cookies. She expects to sell the cookies for $3.50 a dozen. How much money will she make if she sells 12 dozen cookies?

Ⓐ $1.40
Ⓑ $16.80
Ⓒ $6.80
Ⓓ $12.40

10. The soccer team will have a 3-day car wash to raise money. They will wash cars from 3:00 P.M. to 5:00 P.M. on Thursday and Friday. They will work from 10:00 A.M. to 4:00 P.M. on Saturday. How many hours in all will they be washing cars?

Ⓐ 8 hours
Ⓑ 12 hours
Ⓒ 10 hours
Ⓓ 14 hours

11. There are 25 pencils in each of 5 boxes. How many pencils are there in all of the boxes?

Ⓐ 100
Ⓑ 121
Ⓒ 125
Ⓓ 50

12. Eleanor is older than Grace. Samantha is younger than Grace. Leona is older than Eleanor. Who is the oldest?

Ⓐ Eleanor
Ⓑ Grace
Ⓒ Samantha
Ⓓ Leona

GO ON ⇨

Lesson 10, page 3

13. The restaurant where Mario eats lunch sells vegetable soup with oyster crackers and potato soup with wheat crackers. How many different soup and cracker combinations can Mario choose from?
- Ⓐ 3
- Ⓑ 4
- Ⓒ 8
- Ⓓ 2

14. Olga used 6 yards of fabric to make 3 pillows. How many yards of the same fabric will she need to make 8 pillows?
- Ⓐ 24 yards
- Ⓑ 14 yards
- Ⓒ 16 yards
- Ⓓ 10 yards

15. The Nogales family spent $78 for souvenirs at an amusement park. T-shirts cost $18 and vests cost $15. They bought one T-shirt. How many vests did they buy?
- Ⓐ 2 vests
- Ⓑ 3 vests
- Ⓒ 6 vests
- Ⓓ 4 vests

16. Marcia's tennis game started at 4:30 P.M. She finished playing at 5:15 P.M. How long did her game last?
- Ⓐ 45 minutes
- Ⓑ 15 minutes
- Ⓒ 30 minutes
- Ⓓ 50 minutes

17. A normal heart can pump 23.5 liters of blood through the body every 5 minutes. How many liters of blood can the heart pump in 1 minute?
- Ⓐ 0.04 liters
- Ⓑ 4.7 liters
- Ⓒ 47 liters
- Ⓓ 4.07 liters

18. Sam and Jan went fishing. Sam caught a trout that weighed $3\frac{1}{2}$ pounds. Jan caught a trout that weighed $4\frac{1}{4}$ pounds. How much heavier is Jan's trout than Sam's?
- Ⓐ $\frac{3}{4}$ pound
- Ⓑ $1\frac{1}{2}$ pounds
- Ⓒ $\frac{1}{4}$ pound
- Ⓓ $\frac{1}{2}$ pound

19. Jeanine is making bead necklaces as gifts. She made 1 necklace with 36 beads on it and another with 52 beads. Then she decided that both necklaces should have the same number of beads. She would take some beads off the larger necklace to add to the smaller necklace. How many beads would she have to take off the larger necklace in order for both necklaces to have an equal number of beads?
- Ⓐ 8 beads
- Ⓑ 16 beads
- Ⓒ 20 beads
- Ⓓ 18 beads

GO ON ⇨

Lesson 10, page 4

20. The Anderson family is planning to put a fence around their garden. The garden is 82 feet long and 36 feet wide. How much fencing will they need to go around the perimeter of the garden?

- Ⓐ 164 feet
- Ⓑ 72 feet
- Ⓒ 118 feet
- Ⓓ 236 feet

21. Mimi and her friend are planning to visit Washington, D.C., for a 3-day weekend. They estimate they will each spend about $90.00 a day. About how much money will Mimi and her friend need altogether for the weekend?

- Ⓐ $540
- Ⓑ $270
- Ⓒ $90
- Ⓓ $180

22. Lizzie is counting the pennies in her piggy bank. When she counts by 3s, she has 1 penny left. When she counts by 8s, she has 2 pennies left. How many pennies does Lizzie have?

- Ⓐ 34 pennies
- Ⓑ 45 pennies
- Ⓒ 26 pennies
- Ⓓ 52 pennies

23. Michele sold 20, then 23, then 19, and then 26 tulip bulbs to 4 different families. What was the average number of bulbs she sold per family?

- Ⓐ 88 bulbs
- Ⓑ 4 bulbs
- Ⓒ 22 bulbs
- Ⓓ 36 bulbs

24. Laura used $\frac{3}{4}$ cup of milk for a pudding recipe, $\frac{1}{2}$ cup of milk for a cake recipe, and $\frac{1}{4}$ cup of milk for whipped potatoes. How many cups of milk did she use altogether?

- Ⓐ $1\frac{1}{2}$ cups
- Ⓑ $1\frac{5}{4}$ cups
- Ⓒ $1\frac{1}{4}$ cups
- Ⓓ $2\frac{1}{2}$ cups

25. Rosa wanted to walk around the school track 32 times. She stopped to rest after the 24th time. What percent of her goal did Rosa complete?

- Ⓐ 25%
- Ⓑ 80%
- Ⓒ 75%
- Ⓓ 90%

STOP

Your time: _____

Number right: _____

On this lesson I did _____ because _____

_____.

GO ON ⇨

Answer Key

Pretest, part 1, pages 3–5
1. C, 2. C, 3. D, 4. C, 5. B, 6. D, 7. A, 8. A,
9. D, 10. B, 11. D, 12. B, 13. B, 14. A, 15. D,
16. B, 17. C, 18. D, 19. A, 20. D, 21. D, 22. B,
23. B, 24. C, 25. B, 26. A, 27. C

Pretest, part 2, pages 6–8
1. A, 2. C, 3. B, 4. A, 5. B, 6. A, 7. C, 8. B,
9. B, 10. C, 11. C, 12. D, 13. B or D, 14. B,
15. B, 16. A, 17. B, 18. A, 19. A, 20. B

Posttest, part 1, pages 9–11
1. B, 2. C, 3. A, 4. B, 5. C, 6. B, 7. B, 8. C,
9. A, 10. D, 11. A, 12. A, 13. A, 14. C, 15. B,
16. B, 17. B, 18. C, 19. D, 20. B, 21. C,
22. B, 23. B, 24. A, 25. B, 26. A, 27. A

Posttest, part 2, pages 12–14
1. C, 2. C, 3. A, 4. D, 5. C, 6. B, 7. C, 8. B,
9. C, 10. C, 11. D, 12. B, 13. D, 14. C, 15. D,
16. A, 17. C, 18. B, 19. C, 20. D

Lesson 1, pages 15–18
1. D, 2. B, 3. D, 4. A, 5. B, 6. D, 7. D, 8. A,
9. C, 10. A, 11. A, 12. A, 13. B, 14. D, 15. B,
16. C, 17. C, 18. C, 19. C, 20. C, 21. D,
22. D, 23. C, 24. A, 25. C, 26. D, 27. B,
28. A, 29. A, 30. C

Lesson 2, pages 19–20
1. A, 2. A, 3. A, 4. C, 5. C, 6. C, 7. D, 8. A,
9. C, 10. C, 11. D, 12. A, 13. A, 14. B

Lesson 3, pages 21–22
1. B, 2. C, 3. B, 4. D, 5. A, 6. C, 7. B, 8. D,
9. C, 10. A, 11. C, 12. B, 13. B, 14. D

Lesson 4, pages 23–26
1. D, 2. A, 3. D, 4. C, 5. B, 6. A, 7. D, 8. D,
9. B, 10. A, 11. B, 12. C, 13. A, 14. B,
15. B, 16. C, 17. A, 18. A, 19. A, 20. B,
21. B, 22. A, 23. D, 24. D, 25. C, 26. B,
27. D, 28. C, 29. A

Lesson 5, pages 27–28
1. C, 2. C, 3. B, 4. A, 5. A, 6. A, 7. B, 8. A,
9. C, 10. D, 11. B, 12. B, 13. A, 14. C

Lesson 6, pages 29–32
1. C, 2. A, 3. B, 4. C, 5. A, 6. A, 7. D, 8. D,
9. C, 10. B, 11. C, 12. D, 13. C, 14. B, 15. B,
16. C, 17. B, 18. C, 19. B, 20. A, 21. C,
22. D, 23. A, 24. B, 25. B, 26. C, 27. B,
28. B, 29. B

Lesson 7, pages 33–36
1. D, 2. B, 3. A, 4. C, 5. B, 6. C, 7. B, 8. A,
9. D, 10. A, 11. C, 12. D, 13. C, 14. B, 15. B,
16. B, 17. D, 18. B, 19. A, 20. C, 21. B,
22. B, 23. C, 24. B

Lesson 8, page 37–38
1. B, 2. D, 3. B, 4. C, 5. C, 6. A, 7. D, 8. D,
9. D, 10. B, 11. D, 12. C, 13. D, 14. D

Lesson 9, pages 39–42
1. C, 2. B, 3. A, 4. D, 5. A, 6. A, 7. B, 8. B,
9. C, 10. B, 11. A, 12. B, 13. C, 14. A,
15. C, 16. A, 17. D, 18. A, 19. A, 20. C

Lesson 10, pages 43–46
1. C, 2. A, 3. D, 4. A, 5. A, 6. D, 7. A, 8. A,
9. B, 10. C, 11. C, 12. D, 13. B, 14. C, 15. D,
16. A, 17. B, 18. A, 19. A, 20. D, 21. A,
22. A, 23. C, 24. A, 25. C

Skills/Achievement Tests Grid
for Grade 5

	CAT/5 (Level 15)	CTBS (Book B)	ITBS (Level 11)	MAT/7 (Inter 1)	SAT (9th ed) (Inter 2)	TerraNova (Level 15)	TAAS (Level B)
Mathematics Computation							
Using Computation	x	x	x	x	x	x	x
(Adding, Subtracting, Multiplying, Dividing)	x	x	x	x	x	x	x
Mathematics Concepts/Applications							
Understanding Numeration	x	x	x	x	x	x	
Using Probability and Statistics	x	x	x	x	x		
Working with Graphs, Charts, and Tables	x	x	x	x	x		
Understanding Measurement and Geometry	x	x	x	x	x	x	x
Working with Number Sentences	x	x	x	x	x		
Using Estimation	x	x	x	x			
Understanding Number Theory	x	x	x	x			
Working with Algebra	x	x					
Understanding Mathematics Relationships	x	x	x	x	x	x	
Mathematics Problem Solving							
Using Problem-Solving Strategies	x	x	x	x	x		
Solving Word Problems	x	x	x	x	x	x	

Higher Scores on Math Standardized Tests 5, SV 2064-8